THE
LYLE
ANTIQUES
& THEIR VALUES

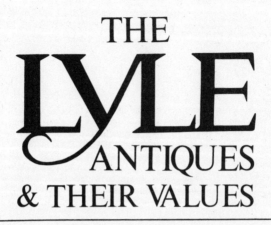

GLASS

Identification & Price Guide

COMPILED & EDITED BY
TONY CURTIS

While every care has been taken in the compiling of information contained in this volume the publishers cannot accept any liability for
loss, financial or otherwise, incurred by reliance placed on the information herein.

The publishers wish to express their sincere thanks to the following for their
involvement and assistance in the production of this volume:—

KAREN DOUGLASS
JANICE MONCRIEFF
ANNETTE CURTIS
TANYA FAIRBAIRN
SALLY DALGLIESH
FRANK BURRELL
ROBERT NISBET
LOUISE SIMPSON
JONN DUNLOP
EILEEN BURRELL

Printed in Denmark by ⑧ Nørhaven A/S, Viborg
ISBN 0-86248-107-4

Front cover illustration
An Almeric Walter pate-de-verre paperweight designed by H. Berge, 8cm. high.
(Christie's)   £9,350

INTRODUCTION

While this series of handy volumes has been specially devised to provide busy dealers and collectors with an extremely comprehensive reference library of antiques and their values, the information will also prove to be of great general interest to those with just a few pieces they wish to sell or appraise.

Each volume is crammed with over 2,000 detailed illustrations highlighting the distinguishing features of a broadly representative selection of specialised antiques and collectibles accompanied by descriptions and prices computed from recent auction figures.

We have endeavoured to obtain a balance between the more expensive collector's items and those which, although not in their true sense antiques, are handled daily by the antiques trade.

The illustrations and prices in the following sections have been arranged to make it easy for the reader to assess the period and value of all items with speed.

When dealing with the more popular trade pieces, in some instances a calculation of an average price has been estimated from the varying accounts researched.

As regards prices, when 'one of a pair' is given in the description the price quoted is for a pair and so that we can make maximum use of the available space it is generally considered that one illustration is sufficient. This will also apply when a description reads eg; part of a service, suite or a set.

It will be noted that in some descriptions taken directly from sales catalogues originating from many different countries, some terms are used in a broader sense than is customary, but in all cases the term used is self explanatory.

Pocket size with a sturdy binding, perfect for use in shops, flea markets and at auctions, *The Lyle Antiques and Their Values Identification and Price Guides* are your keys to smart antique buying or selling.

Tony Curtis

ACKNOWLEDGEMENTS

Abridge Auctions, (Michael Yewman) Market Place, Abridge, Essex RM4 1UA
Anderson & Garland, Anderson House, Market Street, Newcastle. NE1 6XA
Banks & Silvers, 66 Foregate Street, Worcester.
Barbers Fine Art Auctioneers, The Mayford Centre, Smarts Heath Road, Mayford, Woking.
Bearnes, Rainbow, Avenue Road, Torquay. TQ2 5TG
Biddle & Webb, Ladywood, Middleway, Birmingham. B16 0PP
Bloomsbury Book Auctions, 3 & 4 Hardwick Street, London.
Boardman Fine Art Auctioneers, Station Road Corner, Haverhill, Suffolk. CB9 0EY
Bonhams, Montpelier Galleries, Montpelier Street, Knightbridge, London. SW7 1HH
Bracketts, 27-29 High Street, Tunbridge Wells, Kent. TN1 1UU
J. R. Bridgford & Sons, 1 Heyes Lane, Alderley Edge, Cheshire.
British Antique Exporters, 206 London Road, Burgess Hill, W. Sussex. RH15 9RX
Brogden & Co., 38 & 39 Silver Street, Lincoln.
Wm. H. Brown, Westgate Hall, Grantham, Lincs. NG31 6LT
Lawrence Butler & Co., Butler House, 86 High Street, Hythe, Kent. CT21 5AJ
Capes, Dunn & Co., The Auction Galleries, 38 Charles Street, Manchester. M1 7DB
Chancellors Hollingsworth, 31 High Street, Ascot, Berkshire. SL5 7HG
Christie's, 8 King Street, St. James's, London. SW1Y 6QT
Christie's, 502 Park Avenue, New York, N. Y. 10022
Christie's, Cornelis Schuystraat 57, 1071 JG, Amsterdam, Holland.
Christie's East, 219 East 67th Street, New York, N. Y. 10021
Christie's & Edminston's, 164-166 Bath Street, Glasgow.
Christie's S. Kensington Ltd., 85 Old Brompton Road, London. SW7 3LD
Coles, Knapp & Kennedy, Georgian Rooms, Ross-on-Wye, Herefordshire. HR9 5HL
Cooper Hirst, Goldway House, Parkway, Chelmsford. CM20 7PR
Dacre, Son & Hartley, 1-5 The Grove, Ilkley, Yorkshire.
Dee & Atkinson, The Exchange Saleroom, Driffield, N. Humberside. YO25 7LJ
Dickson, Davy & Markham, Elwes Street, Brigg, S. Humberside. DN20 8LB
Wm. Doyle Galleries Inc., 175 East 87th Street, New York.
Dreweatts, Donnington Priory, Donnington, Newbury, Berkshire.
Hy. Duke & Son, Fine Art Salerooms, Weymouth Avenue, Dorchester, Dorset. DT1 1DG
Elliott & Green, Auction Salerooms, Emsworth Road, Lymington, Hants. SO4 9ZE
R. H. Ellis & Sons, 44-46 High Street, Worthing, West Sussex. BN11 1LL
Farrant & Wightman, 2/3 Newport Street, Old Town, Swindon.
John D. Fleming & Co., 8 Fore Street, Dulverton, Somerset. TA22 9EX
Fox & Sons, 5 & 7 Salisbury Street, Fordinbridge, Hants. SP6 1AD
Geering & Colyer, 22-26 High Street, Tunbridge Wells. TN1 1XA
Rowland Gorringe, 15 North Street, Lewes, Sussex.
Goss & Crested China Ltd., N. J. Pine, 62 Murray Road, Horndean, Hants. PO8 9JL
Andrew Grant, 59-60 Foregate Street, Worcester.
Graves, Son & Pilcher, 71 Church Road, East Sussex. BN3 2GL
Giles Haywood, The Auction House, St. John's Road, Stourbridge, W. Midlands. DY8 1EW
Heathcote Ball & Co., The Old Rectory, Appleby Magna, Leicestershire.
Hobbs & Chambers, 'At the Sign of the Bell', Market Place, Cirencester, Gloucestershire. GL7 1QQ
Honiton Galleries, High Street, Honiton, Devon.
Edgar Horn, 46-50 South Street, Eastbourne, Sussex. BN21 4XB
Jacobs & Hunt, Lavant Street, Petersfield, Hampshire. GU32 3EF
W. H. Lane & Son, 64 Morrab Road, Penzance, Cornwall. TR18 2QT
Lawrence Fine Art, South Street, Crewkerne, Somerset. TA18 8AB
James & Lister Lea, 11 Newhall Street, Birmingham.
Locke & England, 18 Guy Street, Leamington Spa, Warwickshire. CV32 4DG
Thomas Love & Son, South St. John Street, Perth, Scotland.
R. J. Lucibell, 7 Fontayne Avenue, Rainham, Essex.
Mallams, 24 St. Michael's Street, Oxford.
May, Whetter & Grose, Cornubia Hall, Par, Cornwall.
Moore, Allen & Innocent, 33 Castle Street, Cirencester, Gloucestershire. GL7 1QD
Morphets, 4-6 Albert Street, Harrogate, Yorkshire. HG1 1JL
Neales of Nottingham, 192 Mansfield Road, Nottingham. NG1 3HX
D. M. Nesbit & Co., 7 Clarendon Road, Southsea, Hants. PO5 2ED
Onslows Auctioneers, 14-16 Carroun Road, London. SW8 1JT
Osmond, Tricks, Regent Street Auction Rooms, Clifton, Bristol, Avon. BS8 4HG
Outhwaite & Litherland, Kingsway Galleries, Fontenoy Street, Liverpool. L3 2BE
Phillips, The Old House, Station Road, Knowle, Solihull, W. Midlands. B93 0HT
Phillips Auctioneers, The Auction Rooms, 1 Old King Street, Bath, Avon. BA1 1DD
John H. Raby & Son, 21 St. Mary's Road, Bradford.
Reeds Rains, Trinity House, 114 Northenden Road, Sale, Manchester. M33 3HD
Russell, Baldwin & Bright, Ryelands Road, Leominster, Herefordshire. HR6 8JG
Sandoe, Luce Panes, Wotton Auction, Rooms, Wotton-under-Edge, Gloucestershire. GL12 7EB
Robert W. Skinner Inc., Bolton Gallery, Route 117, Bolton, Massachusetts.
H. Spencer & Sons Ltd., 20 The Square, Retford, Notts.
Stalker & Boos, 280 North Woodward Avenue, Birmingham, Michigan.
David Stanley Auctions, Stordan Grange, Osgathorpe, Leics. LE12 9SR
Street Jewellery Society, 10 Summerhill Terrace, Newcastle-upon-Tyne.
Stride & Son, Southdown House, St. John's Street, Chichester, Sussex.
G. E. Sworder & Sons, Chequers, 19 North Street, Bishops Stortford, Herts.
Theriault, P. O. Box 151 Annapolis, Maryland 21404.
Vidler & Co., Auction Offices, Cinque Ports At., Rye, Sussex.
Wallis & Wallis, West Street Auction Galleries, Lewes, Sussex. BN7 2NJ
Ward & Partners, 16 High Street, Hythe, Kent.
Warner, Wm. H, Brown, 16-18 Halford Street, Leicester. LE1 1JB
Warren & Wignall, 113 Towngate, Leyland, Lancashire.
Peter Wilson Fine Art Auctioneers, Victoria Gallery, Market Street, Nantwich. CW5 3DG
Wooley & Wallis, The Castle Auction Mart, Castle Street, Salisbury, Wiltshire. SP1 3SU
Eldon E. Worrall & Co., 15 Seel Street, Liverpool.
Worsfolds Auction Galleries, 40 Station Road West, Canterbury, Kent.

4

CONTENTS

Ale Glasses	13	Cruets	58
Apothecary Boxes	14	Decanter Boxes	59
Ashtrays	15	Decanters	60
Beakers	16	Dishes	66
Bohemian	18	Dressing Table Boxes	70
Viennese	20	Drinking Glasses	71
Bottles	21	Drinking Sets	72
Bowls	25	Epergnes	77
American	29	Ewers	77
Bohemian	30	Eyebaths	78
Daum	30	Figures	80
Galle	31	Firing Glasses	81
Irish	32	Flasks	82
Lalique	33	Goblets	84
Loetz	34	Bohemian	95
Pekin	35	Facon De Venise	97
Venetian	35	Powell, James	97
Boxes	36	Sang, Jacob	98
Candelabra	37	Vedar	99
Candlesticks	38	Venetian	99
Car Mascots	42	Honeypots	100
Carafes	46	Humpens	100
Caskets	46	Ink Bottles	100
Centrepieces	46	Inkwells	101
Chandeliers	47	Jars	105
Champagne Glasses	50	Jugs	106
Chargers	50	Lamps	109
Claret jugs	51	Daum	116
Compotes	55	Galle	116
Cordial Glasses	56	Handel	118
Cream Pitchers	57	Pairpoint	118
Cruet Bottles	57	Tiffany	119

Lanterns 121

Lustres 122

Milk Bottles 123

Mineral Water Bottles 124

Miscellaneous Glass 127

Paperweights 130

    Baccarat 134

    Clichy 140

    St Louis 146

Petrol Pump Globes 152

Pitchers 153

Plates 153

Poison Bottles 154

'Quack' Medicine and 'Cure All' Bottles . . . 162

Roemers 165

Rummers 165

Scent Atomisers 165

Scent Bottles 166

    Apsley Pellatt 172

    Bohemian 172

    Daum 172

    Galle 173

    Giles, James 173

    Kaziun 173

    Lalique 174

    Webb 175

Serving Bottles 176

Shades 178

Snuff Bottles 180

Stained Glass 184

Stangenglas 188

Sweetmeat Glasses 188

Syrup Dispensers 189

Syphons 189

Tankards & Mugs 192

Tantalus 194

Tazzas 195

Teapots 195

Tumblers 196

Vases 200

    Argy-Rousseau 208

    Barovier 209

    Beijing 209

    Bohemian 209

    Cameo Glass 210

    D'Argental 210

    Daum 211

    Delatte 215

    Elton 215

    Facon de Venise 215

    Galle 216

    Lalique 224

    Loetz 230

    Mount Washington 232

    Muller 232

    Opaline 233

    Orrefors 233

    Seguso 234

    Steuben 234

    Stourbridge 234

    Tiffany 235

    Venini 236

    Webb 237

Wafer Stands 238

Wall Lights 238

Wine Bottles 239

Wine Glass Rinsers 240

Wine Glasses 241

    Beilby 250

    Jacobite 251

GLASS

The making of glass is a very ancient art with its origins lost in antiquity. Small glass phials and funerary objects have been found in Egyptian tombs of the 4th millennium B.C. but the art of glass blowing, which transformed glass making into an art form with much greater potential, only began to be practised in Sidon, the chief town of ancient Phoenicia, around the beginning of the Christian era. The Romans took up glassmaking on a big scale, establishing several centres of the industry in Gaul.

Examples of glass dating from that era make large sums in auction today. For example, Sotheby's recently sold a Roman dark blue glass cup with a white cameo decoration of a charioteer for £352,000. This type of two handled cup is known as a skyphos and dates from between 25 BC and 25 AD. Only 12 of them are known to have survived. In 1985 Christie's sold a small flask, decorated with the same technique and from the same period, for £330,000.

From Gaul the art of making glass spread throughout Europe and glass works sprang up in Britain, France, Italy, Germany and Spain between the second and fourth centuries.

A famous site for glass making, which is still eminent today, was Venice and at the end of the 13th century the glass factories were ordered out of the city itself because of the danger of fire and re-established on the island of Murano where they can still be found. The products of the Venini factory in Murano are eagerly sought after by collectors, especially by the Germans whose favourite period is the 1950's when glass making at Venini's was at an artistic high.

The Germans have always been keen on glass as an art form for it was in Germany in the Middle Ages that glass making achieved one of its most glorious flowerings. Johan Kunckel got his name into the record books when he invented a technique for making gold ruby glass at Potsdam during the 1680's and between the end of the 18th and beginning of the 19th centuries, the Bohemians invented the technique of making 'sandwich glass' in which one glass beaker, gilded and decorated, was fitted inside another so that the design shone through. During those years the district of Bohemia was known as the greatest centre for glass making in Europe.

A Bohemian ruby-flash glass vase, finely engraved with stags in a woodland, 67cm. high, circa 1850. (Phillips)   *£10,000*

From the beginning, Bohemian glass makers had been both inventive and artistically creative and, unusually for craftsmen at that period, they were not averse to sharing their secrets with glass makers in other parts of the world.

They toured Europe, showing how to achieve their wonderful effects, and this was surprising because craft guilds were notoriously secretive at that time. For good reason, as it turned out, because the Bohemian openness meant that rival copyist glass makers sprang into prominence in many other places, especially in Britain.

Some Bohemian glass makers settled at Stourbridge from where the native glass making industry grew.

As Britain grew more prosperous and the new industrial class had money to spend, glass makers catered for the popular demand with coloured glass table and decorative items. They flooded the market with blue and green glass and especially the highly coveted Victorian 'cranberry' glass which is eagerly collected today.

A Galle blowout vase with overall moulded decoration of flowering clematis, 25.5cm. high. (Christie's) £3,456

A leaded and stained glass panel by George Walton after a design by Charles Rennie Mackintosh, the shaped amber, red and green depicting stylised roses and foliage in wooden frame, 133.6cm. high, 91.4cm. wide. (Christie's) £660

the insatiable domestic trade. Some pieces were deeply incised like jewels or cut with window panels and coloured in blue, green, cranberry or amethyst.

This popularity however meant that copiers took the Bohemian styles and methods and carried them to extremes so that by the mid 19th century, when methods of mass production were introduced, the productions that flooded the market were often over-florid and vulgar in design and execution.

A very rare Lalique glass amethyst tinted car mascot, 'Victoire', 14.7cm. high. (Christie's) £9,680

One of the most popular Bohemian glass makers of the first half of the 18th century was Freidrich Egermann who produced 'Biedermeier' glass marbled in red, green and blue which was copied in vast numbers, and with varying degrees of success, by English manufacturers who turned out decanters, finger bowls and wine glasses for

'Martins Pecheurs', a black Lalique vase, with impressed signature R. Lalique, 23.5cm. high. (Christie's)   *£5,280*

Daum, Legras and Le Verre Francais. In England too a change was underway and artist John Northwood revived the making of cameo glass which had been pioneered by the Chinese during the 18th century. Northwood's work was also shown at the Paris Exhibition.

The art had gone out of the industry but only for a time because things were to change when a new breed of artist appeared, led by the Frenchman Emile Galle.

The French had for many years been producing glass, especially at the paper weight making factories of Baccarat and St. Louis where their mastery of the technique of making oviform shapes with bands of flowing foliage began to be taken up by individual artists in the Art Nouveau period. At the Paris Exhibition of 1878 revolutionary new styles of glass ware were shown by artists like Emile Galle, Antoine

An Almeric Walter pate-de-verre goblet, designed by Henri Berge, 6¼in. high. (Anderson & Garland)   *£900*

An Art Nouveau rectangular leaded glass panel by Jacques Gruber, 256cm. high. (Christie's)   *£9,720*

GLASS

This exhibition marked a turning point in the history of modern glass making for it provided a showplace for an explosion of new ideas and talent.

This had worldwide repercussions and in the Swedish firm of Orrefors, artists were soon experimenting with new techniques and that firm continues to be among the leaders today in certain types of glass. Recently in Stockholm, a vase decorated with brown pandas by Edvin Ohstrom, which he made in 1939 at Orrefors, sold for £53,000 and made a saleroom record for Swedish glass.

A Lalique hanging lampshade, 31cm. diam., signed and dated 1922. (Phillips)   £5,200

A Marinot enamelled glass vase, the clear glass enamelled with a frieze of three nude female figures, 20.2cm. high. (Christie's)   £4,540

'Danaides', a Lalique vase moulded with six nude maidens pouring water from urns, 18.3cm. high. (Christie's)   £1,540

In the U.S.A. Louis Comfort Tiffany at the same time began producing wonderful coloured artefacts from stained glass and anything from his workshop makes mega-prices today when it comes up for auction. Tiffany and the Bohemian artist Loetz copied each other's ideas and also developed techniques of using irridescent glass, as did Joseph and Ludwig Lobmeyr who began painting and enamelling glass and setting it in silver or bronze mounts.

This new Art Nouveau style swept all before it, completely routing the florid designs so loved by Victorian buyers, and the market remained dominated by Art Nouveau designs until the 1930's.

An Art Deco leaded stained glass panel by Jacques Gruber, 70.2cm. wide, 50.3cm. high. (Christie's)   £3,520

These designs are still highly coveted and at Christie's in New York a stained glass panel showing windblown peonies among rocks by the American John La Farge who worked around 1900, set a world record when it sold for £136,723 ($242,000). It is interesting that collectors of stained glass prefer to avoid religious subjects, of which so much was of course produced, but will pay premium prices for more decorative pieces.

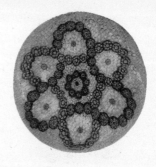

A Baccarat patterned millefiori white carpet-ground weight, 3in. diam. (Christie's) £3,457

Webb cameo glass animal portrait vase signed G. Woodall below the scene and Thomas Webb & Son on the base, 8in. high. (Robt. W. Skinner Inc.) £10,100

A pair of Nancy pate de verre bookends fashioned as dolphins, signed X Momillon, 6½in. high. (Lots Road Chelsea Auction Galleries) £2,500

The Art Nouveau period too saw a new development in glass making when artists began to experiment with the technique of using ground up glass baked in a mould. This gave them much scope for executing unusual designs and at Christie's in Geneva a beautiful head of Cleo de Merode wearing a golden diadem, made by this 'pate de verre' method by the artists Georges Despret around 1907, sold for £35,918.

In England the Art Nouveau glass makers include Harry J. Powell of Whitefriars and

A rare Almeric Walter pate-de-verre paperweight, designed by H. Berge, 8cm. high. (Christie's) £9,350

GLASS

A Venini vase designed by Fulvio Bianconi, concave lozenge shape internally decorated with a 'tartan' pattern, 27.5cm. high. (Christie's) £61,600

A Loetz oviform vase, the body with four dimples, 25.4cm. high. (Christie's) £825

A late 19th century Thatcher Milk Protector. £150

Dr Christopher Dresser of Glasgow but it was Rene Lalique who most successfully provided the bridge between Art Nouveau and Art Deco styles, which first appeared at the turn of the century in the work of the Vienna Secession artists who concentrated on a geometric simplicity of line.

Lalique's work is greatly coveted by collectors today and when his Symbolist nude encrusted with blossoms came up for sale at Sotheby's in New York recently, it was knocked down for $148,500 in spite of being estimated at around $60,000.

Lalique started his career as a goldsmith before branching into glass. His fame became worldwide after he bought his second glass works in 1924 and began to make glass in moulded patterns. He was a very commercial artist and did not confine himself to individual pieces but also turned out much mass produced items like ranges of perfume bottles for French scent manufacturers.

Today those perfume bottles, though made in their thousands, can fetch high prices at auction. His more individual perfume flasks can make four figures. Lalique also made mascots in glass for motor cars for the age of motoring was just beginning. In 1985 his "Spirit of the Wind" of a woman's head with long flowing hair, sold for £1,900 – but a year later, when again presented for sale, it made £3,400.

Other glass working artists to look out for include Kolomon Moser, Joseph Hoffman, Michael Powolny, Otto Prutschere, Sabino, Ething, Hunebelle and Verlys.

And do not forget that there is a brisk interest in more humble glass products – like wine, soda, ink and medicine bottles for example. Early wine bottles are rare and therefore expensive because for many years it was illegal to sell wine by the bottle and it had to be decanted from casks into the buyer's own bottle. Some 17th century wine bottles bearing family crests can fetch four figures.

Even a late 19th century milk bottle like the stoppered 'Thatcher Milk Protector' is valued at £150. No wonder that one of the major spare time occupations of many people in Britain is digging in rubbish tips for old bottles.

ALE GLASSES

An ale glass with bell-shaped bowl on an air-twist stem, 8.3/8in. high.   £100

Georgian ale glass, circa 1750, 4¼in. high. £100

An opaque twist ratafia glass with slender funnel bowl, circa 1765, 20cm. high.   £237

An opaque twist ale or ratafia glass, the slender funnel bowl with hammered flutes, circa 1765, 18cm. high.   £302

An ale glass, the slender funnel bowl with crisp wrythen moulded lower part, circa 1730, 15cm. high.   £352

An engraved mixed twist ale flute, the flared funnel bowl with a hop-spray and two ears of barley, circa 1760, 18cm. high.   £302

Anglo-Venetian ale glass with flared conical bowl, circa 1690, 5¾in. high.   £600

A fine Beilby-enamelled ale glass with deep funnel bowl, circa 1770, 18.5cm. high.   £4,180

An opaque twist ale glass, the ogee bowl on double series stem and plain foot, 6¼in. high.   £385

APOTHECARY BOXES

A walnut cased medicine chest with brass carrying handle, English, circa 1840, 12in. wide.£425

A George III apothecary's mahogany travelling chest fitted with brass swing handle.   £450

Mid 19th century mahogany medicine chest with two doors at the front, English, 8¾in. wide.   £500

An 18th century mahogany apothecary's travelling chest, by Louttit of London, 15 x 10in.   £1,000

A 19th century mahogany domestic medicine chest by Fischer & Toller, 9½in. wide.   £770

Late 19th century mahogany medicine chest with brass carrying handle, English, 10in. wide.£1,000

Antique mahogany apothecary's cabinet with brass inset carrying handle, requiring restoration.   £250

An apothecary's chest, the mahogany case with recessed brass carrying handle, 10¾in. wide.   £638

Georgian period apothecary's cabinet in mahogany case with brass fittings.   £500

ASHTRAYS

A pictorial 'Pirelli' of the
late 1950's and 1960's. £5

Lalique amber glass shell
duck ashtray, 2¾in. high.
£120

An ashtray advertising
'Wuon-Poong' from Korea,
rare.   £10

Castrol Oil glass ashtray.£4

John Smith's Bitter ash-
tray by Wade, England.
£4

An Argy Rousseau pate-de-
cristal ashtray in the form
of a flower calyx, 1920's,
9.25cm. wide.   £350

A Vredestein economy
radial tyre, in current production.   £3

Pate de verre cameo glass
ashtray, signed Walter,
Nancy, France, circa 1895,
3¾in. long.   £500

Buy British Goodrich, from
Leyland in Lancashire,
circa 1920's.   £10

BEAKERS

An engraved spa beaker of lobed cylindrical form, circa 1830, 11.5cm. high. £160

An unusual portrait beaker in turquoise glass, circa 1840, 11cm. high. £935

An enamelled and stained glass beaker with gilt flared rim, circa 1850, 10.2cm. high. £265

A Lobmeyr beaker, the fluted bowl enamelled with a cartouche portraying a lady in 18th century costume, 4in. high. £60

A German Ochsenkopf flared beaker, the sides enamelled in colours with the usual symbols, 1708, 11.8cm. high. £1,296

A Silesian engraved beaker, circa 1740-50, 10cm. high. £380

An enamelled milchglas beaker of cylindrical form, circa 1780, 3½in. high. £140

A 17th/18th century Venetian 'Calcedonia' bell-shaped beaker of blue, green and brown marblised glass, 9cm. high. £462

A pink-stained spa beaker of barrel shape, circa 1840, 12.2cm. high. £250

BEAKERS

A late 17th century
Nuremberg 'Schwarzlot'
beaker on three bun
feet, 8.9cm.   £8,250

Early 17th century Facon
de Venise beaker, probably
Lowlands, 8.5cm. high.
                          £660

Late 17th century Potsdam
engraved beaker with flared
sides, 11.6cm.high. £1,000

One of a pair of Lobmeyr
beakers, decorated with
Arabic script in blue and red
on a gilt ground, 4in. high.
                          £209

A Silesian armorial flared
beaker, the ogee bowl with
moulded and cut flutes to the
lower part, circa 1745, 11cm.
high.   £864

A Venetian Zwischengoldglas
beaker with panelled sides and
a scene of The Last Supper,
after da Vinci, 3¾in. high.
                          £754

Mid 18th century Central
European 'milchglas'
armorial flared beaker,
14.5cm. high..   £660

A mid 19th century Austrian
enamel and clear glass beaker
decorated with a scenic band.
                          £350

Potsdam Royal Portrait
beaker with faceted
everted foot, circa
1720-30, 10.8cm. high.
                          £1,000

BEAKERS
BOHEMIAN

Late 17th century Bohemian engraved beaker with thick-walled sides, 10.5cm. high. £325

A Bohemian engraved beaker, possibly Anton Pfeiffer, circa 1830-40, 14cm. high. £300

An early Bohemian engraved beaker, circa 1700, 11cm. £352

A Bohemian Zwischengold beaker, the flared body with faceted sides, circa 1730, 9cm. high. £715

A Bohemian blue overlay engraved beaker perhaps by A. Pfeiffer, Karlsbad, circa 1840, 13cm. high. £495

A Bohemian 'Zwischengoldglas' and polychrome beaker, circa 1735, 10cm. high. £1,980

A Bohemian amber flash, fluted cylindrical beaker cut with oval panels engraved with named buildings, 5¼in. high. £200

Mid 19th century Bohemian engraved cylindrical beaker with scenes and quotes from The Lord's Prayer, 5½in. high. £314

A Bohemian portrait beaker, the bowl engraved in the manner of Biemann, circa 1840, 13cm. high. £1,210

BEAKERS
BOHEMIAN

A Bohemian amethyst-overlay, cylindrical beaker, 4½in. high. £130

A Bohemian enamelled milchglas beaker, circa 1800, 11.3cm. high. £330

An engraved Bohemian beaker, possibly Eduard Benda, Gablonz, circa 1830, 13cm. high. £1,100

A Bohemian ruby glass beaker, the bowl cut with panels, circa 1850, 11.5cm. high. £245

A Bohemian lithyalin, flaring cylindrical beaker, 4¾in. high. £220

A Bohemian transparent-enamelled chinoiserie beaker, circa 1835, 12.5cm. high. £1,000

A Bohemian 'Zwischengoldglas' flared beaker, by Johann Mildner, 1790, 10.5cm. high. £1,100

A 19th century Bohemian bulbous base glass beaker with hand-painted panel. £320

A 17th/18th century Bohemian 'Tiefschnitt' beaker, 14cm. high. £825

BEAKERS
BOHEMIAN

A Bohemian 'Zwischensilber-glas' beaker, circa 1730, 9cm. high. £1,650

An engraved spa glass, the bowl cut with panels, circa 1840, 5½in. high. £110

A Bohemian engraved 'Rosalinglas' beaker with ovoid bowl, circa 1840, 13.7cm. high. £1,250

VIENNESE

A Vienna beaker of waisted form, painted by Anton Kothgasser, 12cm. £4,620

A Vienna beaker of waisted form, painted by Anton Kothgasser, 11cm. high. £2,310

A Viennese transparent-enamelled beaker attributed to Anton Kothgasser, circa 1820-30, 11cm. £3,520

A Viennese gold-ground enamelled 'ranftbecher', attributed to Anton Kothgasser, circa 1830, 11cm. high. £4,620

A Viennese transparent enamelled 'ranftbecher', the body painted with three playing-cards from a Tarot pack, circa 1830, 11cm. high. £5,280

A Viennese transparent enamelled topographical 'ranftbecher' attributed to Anton Kothgasser, circa 1830, 12cm. high. £4,950

BOTTLES

Taylors Mustard bottle of amber glass, 4in. high. £5

Neo-classic gilded blue glass bottle of lozenge shape, decorated in Giles atelier. £1,000

Venetian 17th century globular bottle with flared neck, 8.5cm. diam. £237

Cobalt blue castor oil bottle, 6¼in. high. £4

A set of three Bristol green spirit bottles and stoppers, with cut shoulders and canted corners, gilt with Rum, Shrub and Brandy, 20cm. high. £400

Zara Seal bottle, 10¼in. high. £12 (smaller examples 4in. high, £20.)

Glass bottle with embossed Madonna and Child, containing holy water, 5in. tall. £12

A 19th century brownish green carboy with gilt scrolled label for Acet Distill, 11½in. high. £220

A rare cobalt blue Hiram Codd's marble stoppered bottle. £120

BOTTLES

1st century A.D. small blue glass bottle with squat pear-shaped body, 3in. high. £700

An 18th/19th century Beijing opaque dark glass circular bottle, 21cm. high. £205

'Figurines Avec Bouchon', a Lalique frosted glass bottle and stopper, 11½in. high. £950

Prices Patent Candle Co. bottle of cobalt blue, 7¼in. high. £30

Warners Safe Cure bottles, amber glass 6¾in. high, £10; Green Diabettes Cure 8¾in. high, £45.

An emerald green Harrogate Wells Spa Water bottle, 8¼in. high. £5

A Galle enamelled glass bottle with silver stopper, circa 1900, 17.5cm. high. £1,430

A Lalique clear and frosted glass bottle and stopper, the cylindrical body moulded with thorny branches, 4¼in. high. £385

Edwardian hair lotion bottle by G. Thomas, 'Extract of Honey and Flowers', £3

BOTTLES

Fishers Seaweed Extract bottle with bulbous neck, 5in. high. £25

Etched and polished internally decorated bottle and stopper, incised Marinot, 13.2cm. high. £3,200

A large Roman green glass bottle with globular bowl, cylindrical neck and everted lip, swirling iridescence, 16.5cm. high. £130

Radam's Microbe Killer bottle, heavily embossed, 10¼in. high. £45

Dutch engraved bottle by Willem van Heemskerk with dark emerald green body, 1689, 33cm. high. £6,500

Heavily embossed Hop Bitters by Taylors of Manchester, 11½in. high. £6

Large glass bottle and stopper by Maurice Marinot, 1925, 33.2cm. high. £10,000

A German silver gilt mounted ruby glass pilgrim bottle, by Tobias Baur, Augsburg, circa 1690, 12¼in. high. £25,300

Opaque white glass bottle decorated in enamels with chinoiserie designs. £1,000

BOTTLES

Emerald green glass bottle
in elaborate rocaille cage-
work mount, with
inscription round neck.
£1,250

A cameo and fire polished
club-shaped bottle by
Emile Galle, 24.8cm.
high. £918

Diamond faceted blue
glass bottle with coloured
decoration of birds,
insects and a fruit tree.
£2,500

'Lynaris' Niagara Patent
amber glass bottle, 8½in.
high. £75

A fine pair of sealed case gin
bottles, 11¼in. high, £40;
4.3/8in. high, £80.

One of a pair of Bohemian
ruby and white overlay glass
bottles, 10¾in. high.
£190

Victorian black glass whisky
bottle with embossed letter-
ing. £25

A Dimple Haig clear glass
bottle, decorated with pierced
plated mounts depicting
Chinese dragons, original
stopper, 10½in. high. £80

Pettifer's Ewe Draught
bottle for safe lambing,
6in. high. £1

BOWLS

A large leaf-shaped bowl by Venini, circa 1950, 'Made in Italy', 33.5cm. wide. £300

A Faberge octagonal two-handled silver-mounted cut glass bowl, Moscow, 1899-1908, 19.5cm. long. £1,030

A marriage bowl inscribed I. Davyz E. Hannaford Maryd. Oct. 30 1769, 21cm. diam. £594

A small bowl of circular section by Francois Decorche-mont, circa 1929, 10.5cm. diam.   £2,970

An Argy Rousseau pate-de-cristal bowl, 1920's, globular body in grey glass mottled in ochre, 6.7cm. £420

Rare circular glass bowl by William Beilby, dated 1765, 5in. diam. £1,500

Orrefors blue and plain cased glass circular bowl, designed by Ingeborg Lundin, 1950's, 6½in. diam.   £300

A 17th century unusual marbled bowl, the ribbed cup-shaped body formed of 'schmelzglas', probably German, 9cm. diam. £495

An Orrefors engraved glass bowl designed by Edvard Hald, 1930's, engraved with young women and naked children.   £825

BOWLS

A Dale Chihuly basket set, composed of a large blown glass bowl with four other free blown 'squashed' bowl shapes, 1980, 37cm. diam. of large bowl.   £3,240

A large spun, brass mounted glass punch bowl and ladle, circa 1910.   £200

Steuben centrepiece bowl with adjusting holder, diam. 12in.   £265

'Limbo for Three', a David Prytherch sculpture bowl form, 1986, 38cm. high.   £3,300

One of a set of four cut glass cylindrical bowls, with silver gilt mounts, the glass circa 1820, the handles with maker's mark of John Bridge, 1824, 16cm. wide.   £1,512

One of a pair of white overlay ruby flash bowls, 9in. diam.   £330

Glossy Burmese bowl, star shaped form with fluted, ruffled rim, circa 1890, 2¼in. high.   £139

One of a pair of 'Lynn' finger bowls and one stand, the bowl 12cm. diam., the stand 15.5cm. diam., circa 1775.   £220

A Schwarzlot decorated armorial deep bowl in the manner of Preissler, Bohemia or Saxony, circa 1736, 25cm. diam.   £3,080

BOWLS

A large Decorchemont pate-de-cristal bowl, 20.75cm. diam., 1920's.   £1,320

A Jacobite two-handled glass bowl with rose and thistle engraved emblems, 9in. high.   £450

A Victorian vaseline glass bowl with an off-white exterior and pink interior, approx. 9in. wide. £35

A Venini handkerchief bowl, the grey/green glass internally decorated with variegated white latticinio design, circa 1955, 22.5cm. high.   £970

A Steuben crystal-footed bowl and cover, 'The Plains', designed by Lloyd Atkins, 33cm. high.   £1,620

A Diana Hobson pate-de-verre bowl form, 1986.   £1,540

A Christopher Williams dust bowl, engraved The Glass-house 1986, 30.5cm. diam.   £462

An amethyst glass bowl and cover, the design attributed to Josef Hoffmann, 12.5cm. high.   £1,100

Art glass bowl, attributed to Victor Durand, diam. 4¾in.   £55

BOWLS

A cut glass punch bowl with Van Dyke edge above a band of diamonds, 16½in. diam. £628

A 17th century Facon de Venise bowl, probably Lowlands, 10cm. diam. £77

A Tiffany 'Favrile' bowl, the gold and violet iridescent glass wheel engraved with maple leaves, 30cm. wide. £770

A Flygors glass bowl, heart-shaped, in clear glass with opaque black inner layer, 1950's, 21.5cm. max. width. £175

A Steven Newell bowl with decoration of Adam and Eve, 1986, 23.5cm. high. £2,420

A Decorchemont pate-de-cristal bowl, 1912. £385

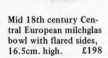

Mid 18th century Central European milchglas bowl with flared sides, 16.5cm. high. £198

A Decorchment pate-de-verre bowl, green and brown marbled glass, circa 1940, 25.7cm. wide. £1,620

Probably mid 19th century cut glass barber's bowl, 26.5cm. diam. £115

**BOWLS
AMERICAN**

Late 19th century cut glass punch bowl, with hobstar cut base, America, 6¾in. high.   £240

A Burmese satin finished toothpick holder, Boston & Sandwich Glass Co., Mass., circa 1885, 1.7/8in. high.   £139

A blown three mould punch bowl, possibly Sandwich, Mass., circa 1830, 8in. diam.   £1,945

Two part cut glass punch bowl, sawtoothed, scalloped rim on bulbous form, America, circa 1900, 13in. high.   £450

Early 20th century American two-part cut glass punch bowl, 14¼in. diam.   £400

Late 19th century two-part cut glass punch bowl, America, 14½in. high, 14¾in. diam.   £629

Late 19th century cut glass pedestal rosebowl, the body with hobstar, crosshatch and fan cutting, 8¼in. high.   £550

An American cut glass fruit bowl, circa 1900, 10½in. diam.   £280

A cut glass two-part punch bowl with scalloped saw-tooth rim, America, circa 1880, 14in. diam.   £690

A Bohemian enamelled
and gilt bowl and stand,
circa 1860, 36cm. high.
£460

Early 18th century engraved
'Goldrubinglas' bowl and
cover, Bohemia, 15cm. high.
£990

Late 19th century Bohemian
rose bowl on stand, 16½in.
high.   £760

DAUM

Daum Cameo glass bowl/
planter, flared wide rim on
squat round body, signed
'Daum/Nancy/France', diam.
10½in.   £893

A Daum bowl, the white,
green and red mottled glass
acid-etched with primroses
and foliage, 13.9cm. high.
£605

One of two Daum Cameo
glass rosebowls, crimped ruffled rim decorated with cameo-
cut sprays of violets, signed
'Daum/Nancy', diam. 7in.
£446

Late 19th century Daum
Nancy acid finished glass
bowl, France, signed, 5in.
diam.   £300

A small Daum bowl with
trefoil-shaped opening,
circa 1900, 9cm. high.
£600

A Daum acid etched cameo
bowl, the clear glass etched
with poppies heightened with
gilt decoration, 25cm. wide.
£495

A Galle fire polished
cameo glass bowl, 8½in.
diam.   £480

A Galle enamelled bowl,
boat-shaped with frilly rim,
engraved Galle signature
incorporating mushroom,
29cm. wide.   £1,210

A Galle cameo glass land-
scape bowl, 9.5cm.,
circa 1900.   £420

Galle carved cameo glass bowl
overlaid with white and deep
rose pink, 6.75cm. high.
          £3,000

A superb Man in the Moon bowl
by Emile Galle, circa 1890,
11cm. diam.   £10,900

An unusual Galle enamelled
glass bowl of milky grey
ground, circa 1900, 10cm.
high.   £1,000

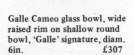

Galle Cameo glass bowl, wide
raised rim on shallow round
bowl, 'Galle' signature, diam.
6in.   £307

A Galle cameo glass bowl
of canoe shape, circa
1900, 13cm.   £440

A Galle cameo glass bowl
in pink/grey glass overlaid
with purple and grey/green,
circa 1900, 28cm. wide.
          £425

BOWLS
IRISH

An Irish 'Canoe' salad bowl on moulded oval foot, 38cm. diam., 28cm. high, circa 1800.   £825

Early 19th century Anglo-Irish cut-glass bowl and stand, 15½in. wide. £280

An Irish salad bowl of oval form with turnover rim, circa 1800, 33cm. wide.   £720·

An Irish cut turnover fruit bowl, circa 1800, 36cm. wide.   £1,400

An Irish cut glass punch bowl in the form of an urn, circa 1800, 32cm. high.   £660

An Irish cut glass circular fruit bowl, circa 1800, 25cm. diam.   £418

Early 19th century Cork Glass Co. engraved finger bowl, 13cm. diam.   £605

Irish cut-glass bowl and cover, with faceted spire finial, 8½in. high. £180

An Irish cut oval turnover fruit bowl, circa 1800, 28cm. wide.   £400

BOWLS
LALIQUE

A Lalique deep circular bowl, 'Saint-Vincent', the blue opalescent satin finished glass moulded with bands of fruit laden vines, circa 1930, 34.5cm. wide. £1,080

'Jardiniere Acanthus', a Lalique canoe-shaped bowl in clear and satin finished glass, 45.4cm. long. £453

A Lalique opalescent bowl, France, circa 1930, 23.5cm. diam. £1,840

A Lalique glass bowl, decorated with five opalescent milky swirling mermaids, France, 11.7/8in. diam. £725

A Lalique glass bowl and cover, 15.5cm. high. 1920's. £400

A Lalique opalescent glass powder bowl and cover, 1920's, 13.5cm. diam. £300

A Lalique bowl, clear and pale green glass, 9.5cm. high. £108

A Lalique bowl, jade green opalescent glass moulded with budgerigars, 24cm. diam. £2,530

'Lys', a Lalique opalescent bowl moulded with four lily flowers, 24cm. diam. £550

BOWLS
LALIQUE

A Lalique opalescent deep circular bowl, 'Ondine Ouverte', 12in. diam. £600

A Lalique clear and frosted two-handled oval bowl, 'Jardiniere Saint—Hubert', 19in. long, inscribed. £280

A Lalique plafonnier, the circular bowl in clear and satin finished glass moulded with bands of fan motifs, 37.4cm. diam. £1,026

A Lalique bowl, the opalescent blue satin finished glass moulded with budgerigars, 23.7cm. diam. £1,296

A circular shallow bowl with everted rim by R. Lalique, 1920's, 11.5in. diam., moulded signature. £230

A Lalique opalescent bowl, the blue opalescent glass moulded with a frieze of budgerigars, 24cm. diam. £1,760

LOETZ

An iridescent glass bowl of squat bulbous form and overall pale gold lustre, by Loetz, circa 1900, 12cm. high. £200

An iridescent Loetz glass bowl of broad shallow form with inverted rim on three white glass feet, 27.5cm. diam. £200

A squat ovoid Loetz iridescent glass bowl, circa 1900, 14.25cm. £385

BOWLS
PEKIN

A Pekin glass bowl with shallow upright sides, mark of Qianlong, 6½ in. diam. £275

One of a pair of 19th century yellow ochre Pekin glass bowls on fitted wooden stands, 4½ in. diam. £275

A Pekin blue glass bowl of deep tone, four character mark and period of Qianlong, 8¾ in. diam. £528

VENETIAN

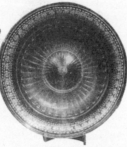

A Venetian deep bowl, on a radially ribbed spreading foot, second half of the 15th century. £1,100

A Venetian shallow bowl with everted folded rim, enamelled in colours, circa 1500, 22.5cm. diam. £648

Late 19th century Venetian pedestal bowl in blotched pink and opaque white and clear aventurine glass, 10½ in. high. £180

Late 16th century Venetian 'ice-glass' bowl, 21.5cm. diam., 14cm. high. £825

A Venetian enamelled shallow bowl, decorated in iron-red, white and blue, circa 1500, 16cm. high. £1,320

Early 16th century Venetian gilt and enamelled bowl, 26.8cm. diam. £5,280

BOXES

A clear and brown stained
rectangular box, by Rene
Lalique, 4in. wide.   £300

An early 20th century Galle
glass box and cover, 3in.
diam., signed.   £900

A Galle cameo glass box and
cover, grey glass overlaid in
orange and red-brown, circa
1900, 15.5cm. wide. £1,210

'Three Dahlias', a Lalique
blue opalescent circular box
and cover of clear and satin
finished glass, 20.9cm. diam.
£324

A Guild of Handicrafts silver
and glass box and cover,
designed by C. R. Ashbee,
with London hallmarks for
1900, 21cm. high, 16oz.
15dwt. gross weight without
cover.   £4,536

A Lalique circular opal-
escent glass box and cover,
1920's, 26.5cm. diam.
£770

'Dahlia', a Lalique circular
box and cover in clear and
satin finished glass, 13.6cm.
diam.   £432

An Argy Rousseau pate-de-
cristal box and cover,
1920's, 14cm. high. £2,860

A Lalique circular box and
cover of flattened form,
25.5cm.   £400

GLASS

BOXES

A Charder cameo glass box with knopped cover, 1920's, 12.5cm. diam.   £125

A Galle cameo glass box and cover of lozenge shape, circa 1900, 22cm.   £770

Glass powder box by R. Lalique, decorated with dancers in Greek costume, 7cm. diam., circa 1920.   £260

A Lalique glass box, the cover moulded with raised blisters and thorny strands, 7.75cm., 1930's.   £200

Cut glass sardine box with silver plated stand and lid, unmarked.   £100

A Lalique opalescent glass box, the circular cover moulded with six chubby birds in flight, circa 1930, 17.25cm. diam.   £225

CANDELABRA

One of a pair of early 19th century bronze and ormolu candelabra, the glass sconces hung with pendant lustre drops, 31cm. high.   £620

One of a pair of Regency ormolu and cut glass twin-light candelabra with flaming finials, 16in. high.   £1,870

One of a pair of Regency ormolu and bronze twin-light candelabra, 13in. high.   £1,296

CANDLESTICKS

Cut composite-stemmed candlestick, nozzle with diamond facets, circa 1765, 23.5cm. high. £250

Pair of early 20th century cut glass candlesticks, by H. P. Sinclaire & Co., N.Y., 14.1/8in. high. £550

South Staffordshire opaque glass taperstick, circa 1760, 18.5cm. high. £250

A baluster candlestick the cylindrical nozzle with everted folded rim, circa 1745, 20cm. high. £583

A pair of Georgian cut glass candlesticks, each with a scalloped urn-shaped candle-cup hung with prisms, 11¼in. high. £1,039

A pedestal stemmed candlestick with detachable wax-pan, circa 1750, 25cm. high. £400

A pedestal stemmed candlestick and a detachable wax-pan, 18th century, 25cm. high. £480

Pair of early 20th century Dominick & Haff sterling silver and cut glass candlesticks, threaded into Classical Revival bases, 13½in. high. £736

A taperstick, the plain nozzle set on a balustroid stem, 5¼in. high, circa 1750. £550

CANDLESTICKS

Unusual glass taperstick of hollow section and with pear-shaped knop, circa 1740, 4½in. high. £300

A pair of early 20th century Steuben green jade candlesticks, 9in. high. £600

A candlestick, the nozzle with everted rim set on a diamond-shouldered pedestal stem, circa 1745, 20cm. £308

One of a pair of Hawkes intaglio cut glass candlesticks, New York, circa 1910, 12¼in. high. £500

A pair of Georgian cut glass and brass candlesticks each on four ball feet, 11¼in. high. £1,178

Early 19th century cut glass candlestick, 9½in. high. £200

Mid 18th century pedestal stemmed candlestick, on a domed foot, 20.5cm. high. £432

Two of a set of four dwarf candlesticks, each with an alternative pink or clear glass shade decorated with flowers and foliage, 9.5in. high. £150

An airtwist candlestick on a domed and terraced foot, circa 1750, 20cm. high. £560

CANDLESTICKS

An opaque twist taperstick, the slender nozzle with everted rim, circa 1765, 18.5cm. high. £2,200

A pair of Charles X gilt metal and cut glass candlesticks and a dressing table mirror en suite, the candlesticks 6¾in. high, the mirror 13¼in. high. £1,210

A pedestal stemmed candle-stick, the cylindrical nozzle with everted rim, mid 18th century, 19.5cm. high. £200

A baluster candlestick, the stem with true baluster section above a beaded knop and triple annulated basal knop, circa 1745, 19.5cm. high. £626

A pair of ormolu and cut glass candlesticks with petal nozzles. 12½in. high. £880

A Lalique glass flower-form candleholder, circa 1930, 23cm. high. £300

A Sandwich Clambroth and blue glass dolphin candle-stick, circa 1820, 10in. high. £176

A fine pair of gilt metal and Bohemian glass candle-sticks, mid 19th century, 15in. high. £4,400

A cut glass candlestick with cylindrical nozzle, circa 1800, 25cm. high. £198

CANDLESTICKS

A baluster stemmed glass candlestick with three graduated knops, circa 1750, 9¼in. high. £450

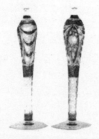

Pair of 20th century Colred cut glass candlesticks, European, 14¼in. high. £326

One of a pair of plain-stemmed glass candlesticks, mid 18th century, 21.5cm. high. £350

A faceted taperstick, the slender diamond-cut column with base knob supporting a cylindrical fluted nozzle, circa 1780, 16.5cm. high. £286

Pair of Georgian cut glass and ormolu candlesticks, each with a scalloped urn-shaped candle-cup over a scalloped dish hung with prisms, 9.5/8in. high. £881

Mid 18th century moulded pedestal stemmed candle-stick, 25.5cm. high. £605

A Tiffany 'Favrile' glass candle-stick in iridescent gold, 4½in. high. £180

A pair of Charles X ormolu and cut glass candlesticks with faceted, hobnail-cut stems, 16½in. high. £2,376

One of a pair of Georgian ormolu mounted, cut and coloured glass candlesticks, 13½in. high. £1,620

CAR MASCOTS

A glass mascot in the form of two leaping Borzoi dogs, possibly Red Ashay, 7½in. long.   £400

Perche, a Lalique glass mascot, script Lalique France marks, 4in. high.   £400

'Cinq Chevaux', a Lalique car mascot moulded in clear glass, etched France No. 1122, 11.5cm. high.
£2,376

A Lalique pink tinted glass swallow mascot, 1930's.   £550

'Spirit of the Wind', a Red-Ashay car mascot on chromium plated metal mount, 11.5cm. high.
£825

'Tete de Coq', a Lalique car mascot, in clear and satin finished glass, 18cm. high.
£1,430

'Coq Nain', a coloured car mascot, the topaz and satin finished glass moulded as a cockerel, 20.2cm. high.
£2,750

Lalique glass car mascot 'Spirit of the Wind', in chromed metal mount, circa 1925, 25.5cm. long.   £1,760

'Saint-Christopher', a Lalique car mascot in clear and satin finished glass, with Breves Galleries Knightsbridge metal radiator mount, 22.5cm. high.
£220

CAR MASCOTS

'Tete de Belier', a Lalique
car mascot, moulded as
a ram's head, 9.5cm. high.
£16,500

A Lalique greyhound car
mascot.   £2,700

A Lalique eagle head
mascot, 1920's.   £750

'Grand Libellule', a Lalique
car mascot in clear and satin
finished glass, 21cm. high.
£3,780

'Falcon', a Lalique car
mascot in clear and satin
finished glass, 15.5cm. high.
£1,870

A Lalique clear and frosted
glass car mascot of 'Victoire —
Spirit of the Wind', 10in. long.
£5,800

'Archer', a Lalique car mascot
in clear and satin finished
glass, 12cm. high.   £1,430

'Grenouille', a Lalique car
mascot in clear and satin
finished glass moulded as
a seated frog, 6.3cm. high.
£3,456

A Lalique car mascot, 'Longchamps', in clear and satin-
finished glass, 13cm. high.
£8,800

CAR MASCOTS

'Victoire', a Lalique car mascot in moulded pale amethyst clear and satin finished glass, France, circa 1930, 24.7cm. wide.
£5,940

Red Ashay glass car mascot in the form of a woman's head, 23cm. wide, 1930's. £400

A Lalique glass sculpture of a fish, colourless, 1930's, 43cm. wide.
£790

A Lalique smoked glass cockerel, 1930's, 20.5cm. high. £500

'Sanglier', a Lalique car mascot in clear and satin finished glass, moulded as a boar, 6.5cm. high. £715

'Archer', a Lalique car mascot, in clear and grey stained glass, with chrome metal radiator mounts, 11.8cm. high. £750

Grenouille, a Lalique glass frog, script R. Lalique France marks (chips to leg and base), 2½in. high.
£1,000

'Pharaoh', a Red-Ashay, car mascot in clear and satin finished glass, 11.5cm. high.
£864

A Lalique glass car mascot, modelled as the head of a cockerel, 8½in. high.
£1,500

GLASS

CAR MASCOTS

'Mother', a corning glass
female head with flowing
hair, 6½in. long.   £80

A Lalique glass dragon-
fly mascot mounted on
a marble pen tray, 16cm.
wide, 1930's.   £1,000

'The Spirit of the Wind',
a Lalique pink-tinted glass
car mascot, 1920's, 16cm.
                        £1,500

A Lalique car mascot in clear
and satin-finished glass,
moulded as a falcon, 16.5cm.
high. £1,540

Lalique pink tinted glass
cockerel mascots, 19.5cm.
high, 1920's.   £800

'Vitesse', a Lalique car
mascot moulded as a
naked female, 18.5cm.
high.   £5,500

Tete de coq, a Lalique glass
cockerel's head (chip to
comb), 7in. high, on glass
base.   £450

'Perche', a Lalique car mascot
in clear and satin finished
glass, moulded as a fish,
9.5cm. high.   £715

A Lalique dragonfly mas-
cot, pink tinted, 1920's,
21cm.   £880

CARAFES

A Venini 'Vetro pesante inciso' carafe, dark brown cased in clear glass, circa 1957, 25.5cm. high.
£770

An Archimede Seguso 'Compisizione Piume' carafe, circa 1960, 29cm. high.
£4,950

A dated enamelled carafe, the opaque white panel inscribed Thos. Worrall 1757, 22cm. high. £6,264

CASKETS

Mid 19th century Bohemian enamelled and ruby glass casket, 6in. square.   £400

A Baccarat gilt metal mounted rectangular casket, circa 1830, 13.5cm. wide.   £280

A Bohemian dated, double overlay, gilt metal mounted, rectangular casket for the Persian market, circa 1848, 15cm. wide.   £2,160

CENTREPIECES

Late 19th century four light rose verre moire (Nailsea) epergne with mirrored plateau, 10in. high.
£260

A Tiffany iridescent glass centrepiece with a design of lily pads, circa 1917, 25cm. diam.   £600

Late 19th century decorated Burmese centrepiece with four nosegay vases, England, 4½in. high. £565

CHANDELIERS

Early 19th century or-
molu and cut-glass
chandelier hung from
a gilt metal corona,
44in. high.   £2,750

Victorian brass three-light
chandelier, 1880.   £103

Circular basket form chandelier, approx. 50in. high
x 24in. diam.   £635

'Mid 19th century cut glass
ten-light chandelier, fitted
for electricity, 65in. high.
                        £4,950

Georgian gilt metal moun-
ted cut-glass twelve-light
chandelier, 43in. high.
                    £10,000

An Art Deco glass and
chromium plated metal
chandelier of star form,
circa 1930, 71cm. wide.
                      £18,700

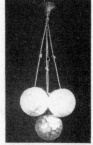

Venetian cut glass triple
chandelier hung with cut
glass drops, 31in. high.
                        £550

An Empire gilt metal twelve-
branch hanging light, fitted
for electricity, 18in. high,
excluding chain suspension.
                          £660

A French Art Deco spelter
chandelier, the opalescent
glass shades moulded with
cell pattern, 72cm. high.
                        £550

GLASS

CHANDELIERS

A cut glass ten-light chandelier, the saw-tooth corona hung with pendant drops, fitted for electricity, 38in. high. £3,455

Early 19th century Empire gilt bronze and cut glass chandelier, 2ft.8in. diam. £1,980

Venetian coloured glass chandelier with baluster stem, 23in. diam. £220

An Empire ormolu cut glass twelve-light chandelier, the nozzles fitted for electricity, 36in. high. £3,240

A Georgian style glass chandelier, of six S-scroll rope-twist arms, 2ft.6in. diam. £1,540

A Regency gilt bronze colza oil ceiling light, the foliate corona, with beaded and faceted drops hung with a cut glass dish, 99cm. drop, 59cm. diam. £8,000

A George III style eight-light crystal chandelier, approx. 41in. high, 34in. diam. £549

Early 20th century hammered copper and bronze chandelier with seven Steuben shades, 20in. diam. £1,785

A 19th century Swedish brass and cut glass twelve-light chandelier, 37in. high, 27in. diam. £4,400

CHANDELIERS

A George III cut glass six-light chandelier with double inverted dish corona hung with pear shaped drops, 50in. high.   £5,280

An Art Deco glass and chromium plated metal chandelier of star form, circa 1930, 71cm. wide.   £6,050

An ormolu and cut glass six-light chandelier, the boss hung with a profusion of pendant drops, 36in. high.   £1,620

A Regency ten-light chandelier with S-scroll arms, 4ft. x 2ft. 10in., circa 1810.   £3,850

An early Victorian brass eighteen-light chandelier in the Gothic style, 56in. high.   £4,950

A glass chandelier, the six branches complete with drops and glass chains.   £420

A Regency cut glass and ormolu chandelier with spreading waterfall drops, 38in. high.   £4,860

A Lalique plafonnier, hemi-spherical clear and opalescent glass, 31.5cm. diam.   £1,100

A large cut glass twenty-light chandelier with scalloped corona issuing eight scrolls with arrow-head finials, 72in. high, 44in. diam.   £26,400

CHAMPAGNE GLASSES

A moulded pedestal stemmed champagne glass with ogee bowl, circa 1750, 16cm. high.
£330

Champagne glass with ogee bowl and plain stem, circa 1745, 16.5cm. high. £150

An opaque twist champagne glass, the double ogee bowl with everted rim, circa 1765, 18cm. high. £825

Opaque twist champagne glass with double ogee bowl, circa 1770, 15.5cm. high. £250

One of a pair of champagne coupes, by Hans Christiansen, 17cm. high. £1,100

One of a set of six Tiffany 'Favrile' champagne coupes, 15cm. high. £1,650

CHARGERS

American cut glass charger with sawtoothed scalloped rim, 14in. diam. £700

A Lalique crystal charger with water lily design, 13¾in. diam., signed. £1,390

'Martigues', a Lalique opalescent glass charger, circa 1930, 36.5cm. diam. £430

CLARET JUGS

A Victorian silver gilt mounted glass claret jug, by E. J. and W. Barnard, 1872, 12¼in. high. £1,760

A late Victorian claret jug, with pink glass body and with domed cover and harp handle, by E. S. Jones, Birmingham 1897, 29.8cm. high. £460

A Victorian silver mounted cut glass claret jug, by Hirons, Plante & Co., Birmingham, 1866, 12in. high. £1,100

A William IV and Victorian silver mounted ruby glass claret jug, by C. Reily and G. Storer, 1836, 12in. high. £5,500

A Victorian silver-mounted glass double-necked claret jug, by Heath & Middleton, London, 1895, 12.1/8in. high. £860

A Victorian silver mounted clear glass claret jug, by Wm. Hutton & Sons Ltd., 1894, 13¾in. high. £1,430

A Victorian silver mounted claret jug. £740

A Victorian silver mounted dimple glass claret jug, London, 1894, 6¾in. high. £187

A Hukin & Heath EPNS mounted large cut glass claret jug, 12in. high. £190

CLARET JUGS

An Art Nouveau pewter and glass claret jug of pear shape with scroll handle, 12¼in. high. £80

A rare ruby-flashed claret jug, probably engraved by Franz Tieze, circa 1880, 33cm. high.   £770

A Victorian claret jug with spire cover, by F. Elkington, Birmingham 1875, 30cm. high.
£770

An engraved claret jug of neo-classical form, possibly Stourbridge for Phillips & Pierce, circa 1880, 32cm. high.   £150

A Hukin & Heath electroplated metal mounted glass claret jug, designed by Dr. C. Dresser, with registration lozenge for 12th November 1879, 23.7cm. high. £6,480

A Hukin & Heath silver mounted claret jug with ebony handle, designed by Christopher Dresser, London hallmarks for 1880, 22.5cm. high.   £1,045

A Victorian claret jug, the cylindrical glass body with swelling base, by Charles Edwards, 1878, 25.7cm. high.
£660

A Webb silver mounted cameo glass claret jug, 1881, 25cm. high. £375

A claret jug, the bottle shape glass body with star-cut base and with a vine branch handle, 27cm. high.
£350

CLARET JUGS

A silver-mounted cut-glass claret decanter of pine-apple cut by Bolin, 35cm. high, circa 1900. £4,904

Edwardian Art Nouveau claret jug with silver hinged domed lid, Birmingham 1905, 10½in. high. £460

An Art Nouveau green glass claret jug with pewter mounts, by WMF, 16½in. high. £290

A Hukin & Heath electro-plated claret jug, designed by Christopher Dresser, 22cm. high, 1880's. £200

An ovoid glass claret jug with a star design, the plain mount with bracket handle, 7¾in. high. £88

An engraved claret jug with plated mounts and hinged cover, circa 1880, 27.5cm. high. £259

A cut glass tapering claret jug with domed hinged cover, 8¾in. high. £99

An engraved armorial claret jug, probably Webb, circa 1870, 27cm. high. £440

Late Victorian cut glass claret jug, by John Round, Sheffield, 1898, 10in. high. £440

CLARET JUGS

A Victorian silver mounted glass claret jug, by Elkington & Co., Birmingham, 1878, 10½in. high. £1,050

A Victorian silver-mounted glass claret jug, by C. Reily & G. Storer, 1846, 12¼in. high. £3,460

One of a pair of silver mounted cut-glass claret jugs, circa 1880, 13¾in. high. £1,750

A Victorian silver mounted claret jug, by Chas. Reily & George Storer, London, 1850, 11in. high. £750

A Victorian plain bellied glass claret jug, by M. G., London, 1883, 7¼in. high. £400

A Victorian electroplated claret jug, by Elkington & Co., with date letter code for 1883, 36cm. high. £242

A French silver gilt mounted tapering cylindrical clear glass claret jug, by Charles-Nicholas Odiot, Paris, circa 1860, 11in. high. £2,268

A 19th century Arts & Crafts period claret jug, by Heath & Middleton, Birmingham, 1893. £240

A Hukin & Heath silver mounted claret jug designed by Dr. C. Dresser, with London hallmarks for 1884, 23cm. high. £810

COMPOTES

Late 19th century New England amberina compote on pedestal base, 9in. diam. £300

Late 19th century amberina footed compote, Massachusetts, 7in. diam. £500

American intaglio cut glass compote, New York, circa 1900, 4in. high. £100

Early 20th century cut glass compote on round foot with starburst base, America, 7in. diam. £120

Part of a Bohemian ruby and white overlay glass dessert service, three compotiers 18cm. high, two 16.5cm. high and ten plates, 25cm. diam. £1,760

Early 20th century cut glass compote with flaring bowl, America, 10½in. diam. £200

One of a pair of cranberry intaglio cut covered compotes, European, circa 1890, 9¼in. high. £360

One of a pair of Portland clear overshot glass compotes, late 19th century, 8¾in. high. £335

Tiffany gold iridescent Favrile glass compote of circular form, 6in. high. £316

GLASS

CORDIAL GLASSES

An 18th century cordial glass with funnel bowl on double air-twist stem to conical foot. £60

A cordial glass with ogee bowl on multi-spiral air-twist stem, circa 1760, 16cm. high. £286

An early cordial glass, the waisted bowl with solid base, circa 1720, 16cm. high. £319

An engraved opaque twist cordial glass, the funnel bowl with stylised hatched and foliate border, circa 1765, 16.5cm. high. £308

A mercury twist cordial glass of Jacobite significance and drawn trumpet shape, circa 1750, 17cm. high. £352

An opaque twist deceptive cordial glass, the ogee bowl on a double-series stem and conical foot, circa 1765, 17.5cm. high. £1,045

Mid 18th century mercury twist Jacobite cordial glass with bucket bowl, 17cm. high. £605

A Jacobite cordial glass with drawn-trumpet bowl and multi-spiral air-twist stem, circa 1745, 16cm. high. £506

A baluster cordial glass, the trumpet bowl with solid base containing a tear, 16.5cm. high. £340

56

CREAM PITCHERS

Glossy Burmese moulded cream pitcher, Boston & Sandwich Glass Co., 1885, 3¼in. high. £244

Crown Milano enamel decorated cream pitcher, Mt. Washington Glass Co., circa 1893, 4¼in. high. £314

An amberina miniature cream pitcher, New England Glass Co., Mass., circa 1880, 2½in. high. £157

CRUET BOTTLES

Opaque glass cruet bottle for Oil, with silver cover, circa 1755-60, 21cm. high. £500

A set of four Bristol blue sauce bottles and stoppers, the bases incised W. R. & Co., and one dated 1788, 11cm. high. £143

Opaque glass cruet bottle for Vinegar, with silver cover, circa 1755-60, 16.5cm. high. £325

An oil or vinegar bottle with a beaded stopper, 15cm. high, and a finger bowl, 12cm. diam. £180

Opaque blue glass cruet, by Northwood Glass Co., Indianna, circa 1900, 7in. high. £330

Mid 18th century Silesian gilt and engraved cruet bottle and stopper, 18cm. high. £300

CRUETS

A George III oval boat shaped condiment cruet, by Wm. Simmons, London, 1788, and a later mustard spoon, London, 1809, 29oz. £1,150

A George III two-handled boat-shaped cruet stand, by Robert Hennell, 1781, the bottle mounts by Wm. Abdy II, 1798, 13in. long, 14oz.11dwt. £1,210

An early George III cinque-foil Warwick cruet on shell and scroll feet, by J. Delmester, London, 1763, 9¾in. high, 23.5oz. £440

A shaped oblong bright cut cruet on shell feet, fitted with seven cut glass condiment bottles, 9½in. £120

A Victorian condiment cruet, by James Dixon of Sheffield. £240

A Victorian cruet, frame by Robert Garrard, 1839, 5⅜in. wide, the frame 22oz.10dwt. £2,890

A Hukin & Heath electro-plated cruet set, attributed to Dr. C. Dresser, 4¾in. high. £45

A plated cruet stand with eight bottles. £100

A Hukin & Heath electro-plated six-sided cruet frame, designed by Dr. C. Dresser, with lozenge for 11th April 1878, 9cm. high. £594

CRUETS

Late 18th century English cut-glass plated and lacquer cruet set, 5½in. square.   £650

A cut glass cruet in the form of an open tourer motor car, 9in. long.   £95

A George III Sheffield Plate oval cruet, the base on shell panel feet, circa 1785.   £340

A Hukin & Heath silver condiment set designed by Dr. C. Dresser, London hallmarks for 1881, 14.2cm. high.   £1,045

A French 19th century oblong oil and vinegar stand on ball feet, 8¼in. high.   £198

Victorian cruet, oblong with central scrolled handle, London, 1852, 18½oz.   £330

DECANTER BOXES

A George III mahogany decanter box, the divided interior with six bottles, an oval salver and two glasses, 10½in. wide.   £594

A Victorian Baccarat liqueur set, in an amboyna and marquetry case, signed, 13in. wide.   £580

A George IV mahogany veneered sarcophagus shape decanter box, the divided interior with two sets of six original hobnail cut glass decanters, 18.5in. wide.   £1,100

DECANTERS

A rock crystal engraved
decanter and stopper,
circa 1880, 30cm. high.
£1,870

An overlay carved decanter
and stopper, probably
Webb, circa 1880, 32cm.
high.   £300

Enamelled glass decanter
by William and Mary
Beilby, circa 1765,
28.8cm. high, with facet-
cut stopper.   £2,500

A Liberty Tudric pewter
and Powell green glass
decanter, circa 1900,
30cm. high.   £220

A Victorian decanter stand with
three oval glass decanters, one in
green, one in ruby and one in
clear glass, by Elkington & Co.,
12in. high.   £572

A WMF silver plated pew-
ter mounted green glass
decanter, circa 1900,
38.5cm. high.   £380

A cylindrical file-cut decanter
and stopper, cut with three
rings to the neck, 10in. high.
£60

A Guild of Handicraft hammered silver and green glass
decanter, the design attributed to C. R. Ashbee, with
London hallmarks for 1903,
22.5cm. high.   £1,296

Green glass decanter
with hammered brass
stopper, circa 1910.
£250

DECANTERS

One of a pair of early 19th century English cut-glass decanters and stoppers, approx. 11½in. high.
£150

A cut-glass decanter with pineapple stopper, circa 1810-15, 35.5cm. high, with a port glass en suite, 13.5cm. high. £1,190

German enamelled decanter jug with pewter cap, possibly Franconia, 1664, 28.5cm. high. £1,250

Late 19th century silver mounted cut glass decanter, with domed lid, Germany, 12in. high.
£225

A Victorian electroplate decanter stand, by Elkington & Co., with design registration mark for 2nd October 1868, 29.4cm. high overall. £330

A George III glass decanter, Indian club-shaped with wide neck, circa 1790, overall height 29cm. £548

A Venini 'Vetro pesante inciso' decanter and stopper, 27.5cm. high. £638

A pair of inverted thistle shape cut-glass whisky decanters with silver mounts, Birmingham 1968. £260

An English jeroboam decanter, the reverse engraved March 8th 1791, 38cm. high. £1,250

DECANTERS

A William Hutton silver mounted decanter, 32.5cm., 1903.   £550

A fine green Bristol glass decanter inscribed 'Shrub'.   £180

Mid 19th century Ford Glass Co. sulphide decanter and stopper, 28.5cm. high.   £600

A 'Lynn' decanter of club shape with horizontally ribbed sides and kick-in base, circa 1775, 23.5cm. high.   £528

A pair of Georgian mallet-shaped decanters facet cut with bull's eye stoppers, 27cm. high, and another matching, 28.5cm. high.   £270

An enamelled Bohemian decanter, the shoulder faceted body painted in tones of puce and white, circa 1860, 30cm. high.   £320

One of a pair of George III decanters with bull's eye lozenge stoppers, late 18th century.   £360

A Venini 'Vetro pesante inciso' decanter and stopper designed by Paolo Venini, circa 1957, 18.5cm. high.   £770

Early 20th century kew blas decanter, Union Glass Co., Mass, 13½in. high.   £163

DECANTERS

A jeroboam armorial decanter of mallet shape, inscribed Carey Stafford, 1777, 40cm. high.
£4,752

A documentary engraved claret decanter with goblet en suite, probably Webb, circa 1860, 18cm.   £600

A Venini decanter and glass, 19.5cm., 1950's.
£77

A French 'boulle-de-savon' opaline oviform decanter and stopper, 26.5cm. high, together with a goblet, circa 1835.   £430

Early 19th century set of three English green glass ships decanters with triple ring necks and mushroom stoppers.   £860

One of a pair of early 19th century dark emerald green cut glass decanters and stoppers of slender club shape, 30.5cm. high.   £550

One of a pair of cylindrical decanters and shaped spiral stoppers, 10½in. high. £55

An engraved decanter of mallet form, the body inscribed Calcavella, circa 1770, 24cm. high.   £572

An Orrefors decanter and stopper, by Nils Landberg.
£1,760

DECANTERS

A Victorian silver gilt
mounted glass decanter,
by Cartwright & Wood-
ward, Birmingham, 1868,
13¼in. high. £860

A Bohemian engraved and
cut decanter, circa 1730,
27.5cm. high. £330

An Irish decanter and
stopper, marked Water-
loo Cork, circa 1820,
27cm. high. £400

A Bohemian enamelled
milchglas decanter and
stopper, circa 1800,
26cm. high. £165

Two George III glass decanters,
classic-shaped with panel-cut
shoulders and bases, circa 1800,
9.7/8in. high and 8½in. high.
£354

One of a pair of cut glass
decanters and stoppers of
club shape, circa 1820.
£432

One of a pair of Irish cut-
glass decanters and stop-
pers, circa 1820, 8½in.
high. £330

A Hukin & Heath 'Crow's foot'
decanter, designed by Dr. C.
Dresser, electroplate and glass,
with registration lozenge for
1879, 24cm. high. £7,776

A Lalique glass decanter,
the broadly shouldered
tapering body with stepped
serrated bands to the base,
24.3cm. high. £100

DECANTERS

One of a pair of green glass decanters, 10in. high. £28

A French decanter and stopper of ovoid form, circa 1850, 27cm. high. £280

Victorian glass decanter, 1870. £52

A Bohemian enamelled 'Milchglas' decanter and stopper, circa 1770, 29.5cm. high. £231

A pair of Georgian wine decanters, one with disc stopper, the other with replacement faceted ball stopper, 14½in. high. £260

English mallet-shaped decanter, bearing the armorials of George III and his consort Charlotte. £4,400

An 18th century English green glass tapered decanter with lozenge stopper. £360

A Netherlands blue-tinted decanter, the metal mounted cork stopper secured by a chain, 25cm. high. £1,800

A James Powell decanter, clear glass, with pear-shaped stopper, 32cm. high. £132

DISHES

A Walter pate-de-verre
dish, 17.5cm., 1920's.
£330

Galle cameo glass landscape dish,
boat-shaped, in amber tinted grey
glass, circa 1900, 13.5cm. wide.
£600

Late 19th century amberina
butter dish in diamond
quilted pattern, 7½in. diam.
£425

One of a pair of Charles X
ormolu and cut glass sweetmeat dishes with ring finials,
the dishes supported by mermaids and tritons, 20in. high.
£4,620

A Schneider cameo glass dish
of circular shape, 39cm. diam.,
signed 'Charder' for Charles
Schneider.   £300

A small rectangular Walter
pate-de-verre dish, 1920's,
11.5cm. wide.   £660

A rare signed Fritsche
overlay dish of circular
form, circa 1900, 23cm.
£1,430

An Irish cut centre dish, the
bowl of canoe shape, circa
1800, 35cm. wide.   £1,210

A large Lalique dish of
deep blue metal by
Phallenes, 1930's.
£880

DISHES

An Iittala glass leaf-form dish, designed by Tapio Wirkkala, circa 1955, 25cm. wide. £400

A Walter pate-de-verre dish, 1920's, incised 'A. Walter Nancy', 14cm. long. £1,870

A Lalique glass circular dish, the sides and centre decorated with moulded daisy stems, 13¼in. wide. £200

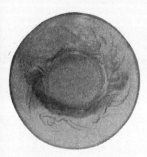

An opalescent 'Ondines' dish, engraved R. Lalique, France, 8in. diam. £310

A Liberty pewter and Clutha glass dish on stand, designed by A. Knox, 6½in. high. £418

A Lalique opalescent glass dish, 'Sirene', signed, circa 1925, 14½in. diam. £650

One of a pair of early 20th century German sterling silver and glass peacock sweetmeat dishes, 6¾in. high. £250

A circular dish, the base moulded radials impressed Cork Glass Co., circa 1800, 18cm. £385

A North Country pressed crystal shaped dish designed as a basket with cane handle, circa 1900, 4in. high. £12

DISHES

Tiffany glass Floriform dish, gold iridescent bowl form with scalloped and crimped irregular rim, marked 'L.C.T', diam. 4½in.   £97

A Barbini clear glass dish, the relief figure of a swimming woman in opaque purple glass decorated in gold, 39.5cm. wide.   £440

An Almaric Walter pate-de-verre dish of lozenge shape, designed by H. Berge, 24.6cm. wide.   £1,296

A 17th/18th century Facon de Venise filigree salt with blue and white decoration, perhaps Antwerp, 6.5cm. diam.   £475

Mid 16th century Venetian bucket or aspersory with rope twist loop handle, 18.5cm. diam.   £1,100

An 18th century cut glass turnover fruit dish, 9in. high.   £420

A glass dish attributed to H. P. Glashutte with enamel painted decoration of a purple clematis bloom, circa 1900, 23.5cm. diam.   £172

A Walter pate-de-verre dish by Henri Berge, 1920's.   £1,980

A 'Non-Such' blue glass dish, by Isaac Jacobs, circa 1805, 18.5cm. diam.   £1,980

DISHES

Late 17th century Facon-De-Venise shallow cup with applied pincered scroll handle, 11.5cm. wide.
£270

A Lalique frosted grey green glass boat-shaped dish, 18in. long.
£360

One of a pair of Regency period rectangular cut glass sauce tureens with Sheffield Plate lids and bases.
£150

Bohemian sweetmeat dish with oval quatrelobed bowl, 10cm. high, circa 1725-35.
£990

A Facon de Venise bucket with loop handles, probably early 17th century, 14.3cm. diam.
£1,760

Mid 19th century cobalt blue blown glass cuspidor, American, 5in. high, 9in. diam.
£156

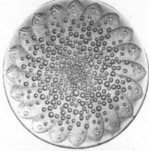

A Galle enamelled glass dish with single flange handle, 1890's, 21.5cm.
£500

A large Lalique circular, blue opalescent dish, moulded on the underside with carp among bubbles, 35cm. diam.
£825

A 16th/17th century Facon de Venise two-handled cup and cover of straw-tinted metal, 11cm.
£880

GLASS

DRESSING TABLE BOXES

A Victorian brass bound coromandel wood dressing case, the silver mounts mostly by C. Rawlings and Wm. Summers, 1845, two bottle tops 1853, case 15 x 10¾in. **£1,650**

19th century burl mahogany travelling vanity case. **£425**

An early Victorian gentleman's dressing case, the contents hallmarked, maker Thos. Diller, London, 1840, 11oz. weighable silver. **£620**

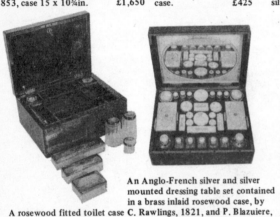

A rosewood fitted toilet case with eight glass bottles and boxes, five with Sheffield plated lids, 12½in. wide. **£100**

An Anglo-French silver and silver mounted dressing table set contained in a brass inlaid rosewood case, by C. Rawlings, 1821, and P. Blazuiere, Paris, 1819-38. **£14,300**

A Victorian dressing case with four glass boxes and seven jars, maker's mark WN London, 1863. **£2,640**

Late 19th century rosewood dressing table box with hinged top and fitted mirror, 12in. wide. **£200**

A small Victorian brass-bound coromandel wood dressing case, circa 1870. **£880**

A Victorian 12in. rectangular coromandel wood and brass bound vanity case, maker's mark J.V. **£300**

70

DRINKING GLASSES

Late 18th/early 19th century green pedestal stemmed wine flute, 15.5cm. high. £1,100

A dram glass with trumpet bowl, inscribed 'The Friendly Hunt', circa 1750, 8.9cm. £110

The 'Breadalbane' Amen glass, the bowl engraved in diamond point, 1745-50, 20cm. high. £28,600

A baluster toastmaster's glass, the funnel bowl set on an inverted baluster stem enclosing a tear, circa 1710, 12cm. high. £352

A Wiener Werkstätte glass, designed by Otto Prutscher, circa 1910, 21cm. high. £1,200

A 19th century crystal glass, the hollow bulbous knopped stem containing a black Swingewood cockerel and hen, circa 1890, 5in. high. £120

A 19th century crystal glass, the hollow bulbous knopped stem containing a Swingewood opal cat and three amethyst mice, circa 1890, 5in. high. £180

A baluster dram glass with short round funnel bowl on a bladed knop containing a tear, 10.7cm. high. £130

A baluster toastmaster's glass on a conical firing foot, 13.5cm. high. £130

DRINKING SETS

Three from a set of eighteen Leerdam drinking glasses designed by Andries Copier, with monogram, 1930's. £400

A Marcel Goupy enamelled liqueur set of decanter and stopper and six small glasses, the decanter 17cm. high, 1930's. £125

Early 19th century glass liqueur set, in a mahogany fitted chest, probably French, chest 11in. long. £548

An Art Deco glass decanter set, the decanter 20.5cm. high and six octagonal glasses, 6.5cm. high. £440

A Patriz Huber liqueur set, white metal and glass, stamped with 935 German silver mark and PH, circa 1900, decanter 18.4cm. high. £2,808

Part of an Orrefors engraved glass drinking set, designed by Vicke Lindstrand, 1940's, the decanter 29.5cm. high. £500

DRINKING SETS

Bohemian gold decorated cobalt blue glass punch set, late 19th century, 9½in. high.
£548

Part of a painted drinking set by Lobmeyr Schwarzlot, circa 1860. £1,250

A set of six Lalique aperitif glasses moulded in clear glass with amethyst tinted panels of Grecian maidens, circa 1930, 9.8cm. high.
£1,134

A Victorian liqueur set with crimped heart-shaped tray, by Heath & Middleton, Birmingham, 1891, the liqueur bottle 8¼in. high, 12.75oz. free. £300

An Art Deco decanter and glasses, the decanter 22.5cm. high and six liqueur glasses 5cm. high (one glass chipped). £150

A Gabriel Argy-Rousseau pate-de-verre eight-piece liqueur service, the tray 40.1cm. wide.
£2,160

DRINKING SETS

Rare set of six gold and enamel vodka charki by Faberge, late 19th century, 4.3cm. high. £20,000

Part of a 20th century set of cranberry over-lay glasses, consisting of eleven water goblets, ten sherbets, eight cordials, and ten finger-bowls with undertrays. £400

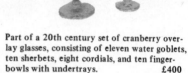

Two Lalique clear glass decanters and stoppers, the spherical bodies moulded with fine vertical ribbing and twenty glasses en suite. £500

A Tiffany iridescent gold Favrile glass jug and four glasses, circa 1910, jug 21.5cm. high, glasses 10.5cm. high. £600

A Japanese cocktail set decorated in high relief with iris, circa 1900. £1,000

GLASS

DRINKING SETS

A WMF electroplated liqueur set and tray, the decanters 9in. high, the tray 16in. wide, all with stamped marks. £480

'Coquelicot', a Lalique globular decanter and stopper, 6¾in. high, and five glasses en suite. £250

Part of an Art Deco liqueur set, consisting of an engraved glass decanter and stopper, the semi-circular body with black decoration, 8¼in. high, and five glasses en suite, 3½in. high, and another three decanters and seven glasses similar. £600

Four liqueur drinking glasses, on tall flaring stems with various sized bowls, possibly Austrian, each 6½in. high. £715

A 19th century engraved wine ewer of ovoid pedestal form and a pair of goblets. £200

DRINKING SETS

A Lalique glass liqueur set, 1930's, decanter 20cm. high. £570

Part of a thirty-nine piece Schott & Gen. Jenaer Glas heat-resistant teaset, designed by W. Wagenfeld, teapot 14cm. high. £800

A Lalique glass drinking set, the decanter 26.5cm. high, 1930's. £400

'Bahia', a Lalique drinking set comprising a jug and six tumblers in clear and satin-finished amber glass, circa 1930, jug 23cm. high, glasses 13cm. high. £400

A Lalique oviform clear and frosted glass decanter and stopper, 7in. high, and eight glasses en suite. £200

A WMF Art Deco moulded glass liqueur set on a stand with moulded handle. £150

Early 19th century glass and ormolu table centrepiece of eight pieces. £440

An Art Deco decanter and set of six matching tots in smoked and frosted glass. £85

EPERGNES

A Victorian epergne with
four milky red trumpet
vases, 1ft.10½in. high.
£120

A cranberry triple trumpet-
shaped three-branch blown
glass epergne on circular
crimped base. £280

A Victorian glass epergne,
opaline and green tinted
decoration, 23in. high.
£260

EWERS

A Richardson vitrified
ewer, enamel painted in
shades of grey with water-
carriers by a fountain,
registration lozenge for
1843, 24.5cm. high.
£345

A Continental silver mounted
ewer, the silver cap with
embossed fruit decoration, on
a lead crystal base, 10in. high.
£95

A Galle oviform single-
handled ewer, the silver
mount modelled with styl-
ized flowers, signed, 10¼in.
high. £820

A claret jug of ewer
shape with oval glass body,
by C.E., London, 1896,
14in. high. £1,250

Royal Flemish ewer by
Mt. Washington Glass Co.,
circa 1890, 8½in. high.
£1,200

Mid 16th century Venetian
filigree ewer, the whole in
'vetro a reticello' 37.6cm.
high. £4,180

EYE BATHS

Green glass eye bath, made in England. £2.50

'Optrex Safeguards Sight', blue glass eye bath.　£2

Clear glass squat ribbed eye bath. £5

Clear glass stemmed eye bath with wrythened bowl.　£8

Wyeth Collyrium soothing eye lotion with eye bath stopper. £30

Milkglass stemmed eye bath. £10

Pedestal moulded green glass eye bath.　£5

Clear glass cottage-loaf eye bath with reservoir.　£3

An early green freeblown eye bath with embellished stem. £20

EYE BATHS

Cobalt blue glass
eye bath, made in
England.   £3.50

Maw's Eye Douche with
rubber ball.   £20

Squat pink glass eye bath by
Maws of London.   £4

A large bowled blue freeblown
eye bath.   £20

Clear waisted glass eye bath. £5

Stemmed moulded amber glass
eye bath.   £15

Blue glass short stemmed
freeblown eye bath.   £20

Blue glass eye bath with
reservoir and foot.
            £30

Clear glass eye bath
on stand.   £2

FIGURES

An Etling opalescent figure of a semi naked woman, 11in. high.   £480

North Country machine-pressed milk glass oval butter dish cover on wood plinth, 2.5in. wide.   £10

Lalique frosted glass mascot, 'Crouching Mermaid', 4in. high.   £230

A Lalique glass figure of a naked woman with a wreath of flowers falling to her feet, circa 1935, 21cm. high.   £300

A Lalique frosted glass figure on bronze base, Suzanne, 23cm. high without base.   £4,180

A Salviati glass sculpture designed by Livio Seguso, 1960, 61.5cm. high. £440

A sea-blue frosted and bubbled glass figure of Pierrot, by Walter Nancy, France. 9½in. high.   £1,100

'Cote d'Azur Pullman Express', a Lalique figure, the clear satin finished glass moulded as a naked maiden, 16.8cm. high.   £3,080

Lalique glass head of a woman, on stepped circular wooden base, 1930's, 37cm. high.   £990

FIRING GLASSES

Deceptive firing glass
with thickened flared
bowl, circa 1740-60,
4in. high.   £275

Beilby Masonic firing glass,
ogee bowl enamelled in
white and iron-red,
circa 1770, 8cm. high.
                    £1,000

Mid 18th century Jaco-
bite firing glass, 10cm.
high.   £216

A firing glass with drawn-
trumpet bowl inscribed 'The
Friendly Hunt', circa 1750,
9cm. high.   £165

A Jacobite firing glass or
syllabub glass set on a hollow
knop and everted foot, circa
1750, 10cm. high.   £505

A colour twist firing glass
with ogee bowl, on a ter-
raced foot, circa 1770,
10.5cm. high.   £1,836

Masonic firing glass
of drawn trumpet
shape, 3¾in. high.
                £200

A Jacobite firing glass, the
small ogee bowl engraved
with crowned thistle, on
thick circular foot, circa
1760, 9cm. high.   £990

A firing glass of possible
Jacobite significance, circa
1760, 11.5cm. high.   £165

FLASKS

A gimmel flask in ruby glass with a wavy combed design in red and opaque white, 24cm. long. £60

A vertically ribbed chestnut flask, golden amber, sheared mouth-pontil scar, 4½in. high, 1820-40. £112

17th century Spanish Facon de Venise flask with hexa-lobed body, 18.5cm. high. £350

Dockhead black glass flask by Wm. Jackson, 7¾in. long. £150

A Documentary Waterford flask of elliptical form with short cylindrical neck, circa 1783-1799, 20.5cm. long. £730

A 17th/18th century South German pewter mounted spirit flask, 15.5cm. high. £1,870

A 16th century Bohemian enamelled flask, the body painted in colours, 16.5cm. high. £550

A 17th century Bohemian enamelled small pewter mounted blue flask, 8cm. high. £2,860

A Masonic eagle historical pint flask, golden amber, White Glass Works, 1820-40. £193

GLASS

FLASKS

A Venetian armorial
pilgrim flask decorated
in coloured enamels of
Bentivoglio, circa 1492,
35.5cm. high. £8,800

A 17th century spirit flask
(Tonnelet) of barrel shape,
Low Countries or France,
11.5cm. wide.   £385

A mid 19th century Nailsea
red, white and blue bellows
flask, 12½in. high.   £158

Late 18th century amethyst
flask, the globular body
moulded with 'nipt diamond
waves', 20cm. high. £702

A flask of flattened oviform
shape, the sides with a band
of trailed loop ornament above
'nipt diamond waves', circa
1695, 13.5cm. high. £528

An 18th century Central
European enamelled pewter
mounted rectangular spirit
flask, 20cm. high.   £330

One of two half pint Adams-
Jefferson portrait flasks, GI-
114, olive amber, sheared
mouth-pontil scars, 1830-50.
                          £147

A scroll pint flask, GIX-11,
golden amber, sheared
mouth-pontil scar, 1845-60.
                          £140

A double eagle historical
pint flask, GII-40, bright
green, sheared mouth-pontil
scar, Kensington Glass Works,
1830-38.   £193

83

A Commemorative goblet with rounded funnel bowl, the glass circa 1710, engraving later, 20.5cm. £2,200

An incised twist goblet of emerald green tint, circa 1760, 14cm. high. £528

A Low Countries opaque twist goblet engraved in diamond-point, circa 1790, 17.5cm. high. £864

A baluster goblet with bell bowl, the stem with two true baluster sections, circa 1710, 17.5cm. high. £264

A Potsdam armorial goblet and cover, circa 1720, 41cm. high. £715

An armorial light baluster goblet, on a multi-knopped stem and domed foot, circa 1755, 19cm. high. £388

An engraved light baluster goblet, the bowl with seven arrows tied by ribbon representing the Seven Provinces of the Netherlands, circa 1760, 18.5cm. high. £756

A Jacobite goblet, the bucket bowl engraved with rose, half-opened and closed buds, moth on reverse, circa 1750, 17.5cm. high. £264

A Dutch-engraved wine goblet, the bowl supported on a fine Newcastle-type light baluster stem, circa 1750, 21cm. high. £1,320

GOBLETS

A baluster goblet with funnel bowl, inscribed L. Watson, circa 1710, 20.8cm.
£572

Dutch-engraved goblet with bellbowl on flattened knop and domed foot, 14cm. high.
£450

A baluster goblet with pointed double-ogee bowl, circa 1700, 21cm.
£1,760

A baluster goblet, the funnel bowl supported on an inverted baluster stem, circa 1720, 17cm. high.
£324

A German Royal armorial goblet and a cover, the glass possibly Thuringia, the engraving Potsdam, 1720-25, 32cm. high overall. £1,760

A colour twist goblet with an ogee bowl, circa 1765, 19.5cm. high.
£1,980

An engraved pedestal stemmed goblet with round funnel bowl, circa 1750, 17.5cm. high.
£506

A light baluster betrothal goblet, the funnel bowl decorated in the manner of David Wolff, late 18th century, 19.2cm. high.
£3,024

A baluster goblet, the funnel bowl supported on an inverted baluster stem, circa 1720, 20.5cm. high.
£259

GOBLETS

A 17th century Facon de Venise goblet of smokey metal, 15.5cm. high. £440

An airtwist Jacobite goblet engraved with a spray of Scotch thistle and forget-me-not, circa 1750, 19.5cm. high. £453

An early goblet with rounded bowl on a hollow inverted baluster stem, circa 1690, 21cm. high. £594

A mammoth baluster goblet, the funnel bowl with a solid lower part, circa 1710, 30.5cm. high. £1,980

A Vienna Secession glass goblet attributed to Moser and the design to J. Hoffmann, circa 1915, 12.8cm. high. £270

Mid 18th century engraved composite stemmed goblet with bell bowl, 21.5cm. high. £1,430

A baluster goblet with straight-sided funnel bowl, circa 1705, 18cm. high. £496

A mid 18th century light baluster Royal armorial goblet with multi-knopped stem, 20.5cm. high. £1,620

A mid 18th century German armorial goblet with funnel bowl, 19cm. high. £302

86

GOBLETS

Saxon Royal Marksmanship goblet with engraved funnel bowl, circa 1719, 21.5cm. high.   £750

An unusual bell goblet, probably German, circa 1730, 18.7cm. high.
                    £396

A goblet with bucket-shaped bowl, on Silesian stem, 7in. high.   £65

A light baluster armorial goblet engraved by the mono-grammist JB, circa 1750, 22.3cm. high.   £3,240

A Wiener Werkstatte glass goblet, the design attributed to Dagobert Peche, 8.4cm. high.   £220

A plain stemmed goblet, the bucket bowl inscribed Success to Sir Francis Knollys, circa 1760, 19.5cm. high.   £330

A facet cut shipping goblet attributed to Simon J. Sang, 1770-80, 23.5cm. high.
                    £2,592

An engraved colour-twist goblet with large ogee bowl, possibly Jacobite, circa 1770, 18cm. high.   £1,540

A baluster goblet, the thistle bowl supported on a cushion above a drop knopped sec-tion, circa 1700, 15.5cm. high.   £756

GOBLETS

Dutch-engraved New-castle goblet on knopped stem.   £6,000

Goblet of emerald-green tint, bowl with vertical ribs, circa 1760, 12cm. high.   £200

A baluster goblet with funnel bowl set on a cushion knop, circa 1720, 23.8cm. high.   £330

An engraved goblet with large ogee bowl, the stem enclosing an opaque-white gauze corkscrew, circa 1760, 19.2cm. high.   £165

A baluster goblet with a funnel bowl, circa 1700, 17.5cm. high.   £324

A baluster goblet, the bell bowl supported on an annulated knop above a true baluster stem and short plain section, circa 1715, 21cm. high.   £418

A composite stemmed engraved goblet with round funnel bowl with fruiting vinestock, 19cm. high.   £280

An emerald green incised twist goblet with cup-shaped bowl, circa 1765, 14cm. high.   £1,320

An engraved goblet set on a facet-cut stem with conical foot, circa 1780, 18cm. high.   £154

GOBLETS

One of three engraved
Lauenstein goblets, late
18th century, 18cm.
high.   £1,026

An enamelled and gilt
'Annagrun' goblet with
faceted ovoid bowl, circa
1840, 13cm. high. £200

A Royal Armorial goblet
of Newcastle type with
pointed funnel bowl,
circa 1745, 19cm.
                £1,870

A baluster goblet on a folded
conical foot, circa 1700,
17.5cm. high.   £345

A Jacobite portrait goblet,
the bowl engraved with a
half-length portrait of
Prince Charles Edward,
circa 1750, 19.5cm. high.
                £3,740

A calligraphic baluster goblet, attributed to Bastiaan
Boers or Francois Crama,
the rim engraved in diamond-
point, circa 1700, 17.8cm.
high.   £5,940

A baluster goblet with a
round funnel bowl, the solid
lower part with a tear, circa
1710, 16.5cm. high.   £528

A Silesian engraved goblet
with fluted oviform bowl,
circa 1760, 16cm. high.
                £594

A Dutch stiple-engraved
Friendship goblet, the bowl
supported on a facet-cut
stem, circa 1770, 21.7cm.
high.   £3,630

GOBLETS

A Potsdam engraved goblet with deep funnel bowl, circa 1710, 22cm. £220

A baluster goblet with deep bowl and slightly flared sides, circa 1710, 21cm. £550

A Dutch engraved armorial goblet with thistle-shaped bowl, circa 1750, 20cm. high. £324

A large armorial goblet, the funnel bowl engraved with the arms of Delfland, circa 1780, 23cm. high. £648

An Almeric Walter pate-de-verre goblet, designed by Henri Berge, 6¼in. high. £900

A baluster goblet, the funnel bowl supported on an inverted baluster stem above a folded conical foot, circa 1720, 18cm. high. £324

A baluster goblet with straight-sided funnel bowl, circa 1715, 16.5cm. high. £220

A baluster goblet, the funnel bowl supported on a cushion knop, circa 1710, 20.5cm. high. £453

A facet stemmed engraved goblet with funnel bowl, circa 1785, 19.5cm. high. £286

GOBLETS

A Potsdam/Zechlin engraved and gilt Royal goblet, circa 1730, 22cm. high.   £1,320

A gilt overlay goblet in green and red, circa 1840, 14cm. high.   £220

A late 18th century Russian engraved goblet with ovoid bowl, 19.8cm.   £385

A stipple engraved goblet on a 19th century replacement parcel gilt lower section, by Frans Greenwood, circa 1744, 24.3cm. high overall. £32,400

A gilt decorated emerald green goblet with cup-shaped bowl, circa 1765, 14cm. £935 high.

A semi-polychrome enamelled opaque twist goblet with ogee bowl, circa 1775, 17.5cm. high.   £1,540

A baluster goblet with bell bowl supported on a triple annulated knop, circa 1720, 18cm. high.   £324

A Richardson vitrified goblet with baluster stem, enamel painted in shades of gray with water carriers, 17cm. high.   £129

Mid 18th century Newcastle light baluster engraved goblet, the bell bowl with a border of laub-und-Bandelwerk, 17cm. high.   £330

GOBLETS

A baluster goblet, the round funnel bowl with a tear to the solid lower part, circa 1715, 15.5cm. high. £220

A Dutch Friendship goblet with funnel bowl, circa 1755, 18cm. high. £259

Mid 18th century Newcastle engraved composite stemmed goblet on a folded conical foot, 16.5cm. high. £286

A mid 18th century hunting goblet, the engraving perhaps by a German hand, 22.5cm. high. £3,240

An engraved composite-stem goblet, the bowl supported on a blade knop over inverted baluster stem, circa 1765, 19cm. high. £495

A baluster goblet with a slender thistle-shaped bowl, circa 1705, 17.5cm. high. £810

Engraved goblet with bell bowl and knopped stem, circa 1740-60, 19cm. high. £500

A pedestal stemmed armorial goblet engraved by Willem O. Robart, 1735-45, 20cm. high. £1,566

English engraved glass goblet with rounded funnel bowl, 1745, 18.4cm. high. £400

GOBLETS

An armorial baluster goblet
with bucket bowl, circa
1760, 16cm. high.   £1,296

A heavy baluster goblet, the
ovoid bowl drawn from a
stem terminating in an angular knop, circa 1710, 17.5cm.
high.   £1,210

A Dutch-engraved goblet
with pointed funnel bowl,
circa 1750, 18cm. high.
£506

An engraved light baluster
goblet, the stem with beaded
dumb-bell section, circa 1755,
21cm. high.   £1,836

Early 18th century German
engraved double bowled
goblet, 18.5cm. high. £462

A baluster goblet, the stem
with a wide angular knop,
circa 1715, 16.5cm. high.
£280

A Dutch engraved goblet,
with a folded conical foot,
circa 1750, 24cm. high.
£528

A 'single flint' goblet, the
straight-sided funnel bowl
with a solid lower part,
circa 1700, 18cm. high.
£550

A Royal armorial light
baluster goblet, the bowl
engraved with the crowned
arms of William V, circa
1760, 21cm. high. £648

GOBLETS

Mid 18th century Saxon 'friendship' goblet and cover, with inscription, 31cm. high   £1,000

An overlay spa glass with shaped bowl on splayed foot, circa 1840, 13cm.   £90

A baluster wine goblet with deep bell bowl, circa 1710, 18cm.   £154

A pedestal stemmed goblet with straight-sided funnel bowl, circa 1750, 16cm. high.   £352

A pair of topographical goblets with bell bowls, circa 1765, 22cm. high.   £3,780

Late 17th century Netherlands diamond engraved goblet, 14.5cm. high.   £1,540

A baluster goblet with round funnel bowl on a small knop, on a conical folded foot, 20cm. high.   £400

A Silesian mercantile goblet and cover perhaps for the Dutch market, circa 1745, 27cm. high.   £4,620

A pedestal stemmed Alliance goblet in the manner of Robart, 1735-40, 19cm. high.   £1,134

GOBLETS
BOHEMIAN

An engraved overlay spa goblet with barrel-shaped bowl, circa 1840, 16.5cm.
£120

A Bohemian Zwischengold goblet, circa 1730, 16.5cm. high.
£770

A large Bohemian amber-flash 'souvenir' goblet on a fluted stem, circa 1860, 23.5cm. high.
£200

A Bohemian dated green and enamelled goblet and cover, the fluted bowl decorated in silver, 1841, 25.5cm. high.
£1,100

Pair of 19th century overlaid and cut Bohemian covered goblets, 19in. high.
£1,900

A Bohemian engraved ruby and clear glass goblet in the manner of Karl Pfohl, circa 1855, 22cm. high.
£715

Mid 19th century Bohemian dark-blue glass goblet and cover, 35.4cm. high.
£600

An Austrian/Bohemian enamelled glass goblet, 1840's, 13cm. high.
£400

A Bohemian ruby glass goblet and cover cut in Tiefschnitt technique with stags and birds, 61.5cm., 1850's.
£1,925

GOBLETS
BOHEMIAN

An engraved Bohemian goblet
and cover, 38.5cm. high.
£880

A Bohemian engraved and
stained ruby goblet, circa
1860, 23cm. high. £550

Mid 19th century Bohemian
ruby stained bell-shaped
glass goblet and cover.
£2,700

A Bohemian transparentemail goblet,
decorated in transparent enamels in
shades of pink and amber with fish,
circa 1840, 14.5cm. high.   £540

A Bohemian hyalith goblet
with gilt interior, Count
Buquoy's Glassworks, circa
1835, 12.5cm. high. £669

A Bohemian engraved amber
flash goblet, the flared fluted
bowl on a fluted knopped
stem, circa 1840, 26cm. high.
£550

Late 17th century Bohemian
Facon De Venise wine goblet,
16.5cm. high.   £500

A N. Bohemian (Haida)
engraved amber flash goblet
and cover, perhaps by F.
Egermann Jnr., circa 1845,
44.5cm. high.   £2,860

An amber-flash Williamite
goblet, probably Bohemian,
circa 1840, 14.4cm. high.
£180

GOBLETS
FACON DE VENISE

17th century Low Countries or German Facon de Venise wing-stem goblet, 15.9cm. high.   £440

A Lowlands Facon de Venise engraved serpent-stem goblet, circa 1650, 23.2cm. high.   £3,740

A 17th century Lowlands Facon de Venise serpent-stem goblet, 23cm. high.   £440

A 17th century Facon de Venise serpent-stem goblet, 23.2cm. high.   £1,760

A 17th century Facon-De-Venise serpent stemmed goblet, Venice or Netherlands, 31cm. high.   £1,760

Late 17th century Facon-de-Venise diamond engraved serpent stemmed goblet, 18cm. high.   £605

POWELL, JAMES

A James Powell flower form goblet, milky vaseline glass, the flower form bowl with frilly rim, 30cm. high. £770

A James Powell flower-form goblet, milky vaseline-coloured glass. 30.5cm. high.   £918

A James Powell goblet, milky vaseline glass, 21cm. high.   £275

GOBLETS
SANG, JACOB

A light baluster goblet by Jacob Sang, supported on a waist-knopped section above a beaded inverted baluster stem, 1755-65, 19cm. high. £1,512

A composite stemmed goblet by Jacob Sang, on a conical foot, circa 1760, 19.5cm. high. £4,104

A light baluster armorial goblet by Jacob Sang, the funnel bowl engraved with the crowned arms of Prussia, circa 1765, 19.5cm. high. £1,404

A light baluster friendship goblet by Jacob Sang, on a conical foot, 1755-60, 19.5cm. high. £2,160

A composite stemmed shipping goblet by Jacob Sang, supported on a knopped section filled with airtwist spirals, 1760-70, 19.5cm. high. £4,860

A composite stemmed goblet by Jacob Sang, supported on a beaded dumb-bell section above an inverted baluster stem, 1759, 18.3cm. high. £5,184

A composite stemmed marriage goblet by Jacob Sang, on a conical foot, circa 1760, 19.5cm. high. £2,160

A betrothal goblet by Jacob Sang, supported on a waist-knopped section above a beaded inverted baluster stem, 1755-60, 18.5cm. high. £1,944

An opaque twist shipping goblet attributed to Jacob Sang, circa 1785, 19.5cm. high. £3,456

GOBLETS
VEDAR

One of a set of six large Vedar goblets with cylindrical stems and hemispherical bowls, 8in. high. £1,000

One of six large Vedar goblets, enamel painted with a continuous frieze of dancing putti with floral garlands. 19.4cm. high. £1,296

One of three large Vedar glass goblets, the bowls enamel painted with continuous frieze of naked females and peacocks, 7½in. high, signed XVII. £682

VENETIAN

A 16th century Venetian goblet of greyish metal with bell-shaped bowl, 15cm. high. £2,310

Early 17th century Venetian goblet in slightly greyish metal, 19.5cm. high. £1,320

One of a pair of Venetian ruby glass goblets with panels of The Road to Calvary, 9in. high. £345

Late 19th century Venetian goblet in pale pink and clear aventurine glass, 15½in. high. £240

Late 19th century Venetian goblet vase in nacreous marbled pink and amber, and clear aventurine glass, 12½in. high. £170

Early lead glass goblet in Venetian style, supported on wrythen serpentine stem, circa 1680, 9¾in. high. £850

99

HONEYPOTS

George III silver gilt
mounted beehive
honey-pot, cover and
stand, circa 1800-
1803. £1,000

A pair of early 19th century urn-
shaped honey jars with domed
covers and cut knop finials,
12in. high, overall. £320

Late 19th century silver
mounted cut glass beehive
honey-pot, unmarked, 8¾in.
high. £5,750

HUMPENS

A German enamelled 'Reichsadler' humpen of greenish
metal, dated 1678, Bohemia,
28cm. high. £1,980

A Bohemian pewter and
porcelain mounted ruby
overlay tankard and cover,
engraved in the manner of
Pfhol, circa 1860, 25cm.
high. £396

A German 'Reichsadler'
humpen of greenish-grey tint,
Bohemia, dated 1601, 28.5cm.
high. £8,800

INK BOTTLES

A cobalt blue Blackwood &
Co. Patent Syphon Ink bottle,
4¾in. high. £75

19th century octagonal
glass ink bottle. £4

Blackwoods of London, aqua
glass igloo ink bottle with embossed Registry of Designs
diamond. £15

INKWELLS

Barrel shaped glass inkwell with cross hatched body.£12

Aqua glass inkwell in the form of a beehive made from coiled straw with opening at the base.   £100

A rare cobalt blue glass tent inkwell.   £50

Capstan shaped glass inkwell with concave sides, 5cm. high.   £10

An extremely rare deep green glass turtle or sunflower ink-well, possibly French.   £200

Plain aqua glass inkwell of bulbous conical shape, 6cm. high.   £6

Aqua glass cottage inkwell with cross hatched roof and no side embossing, 6cm. high.   £70

An aqua glass segmented ink-well.   £10

Aqua glass cottage inkwell with water butt and stippled roof decoration, 6cm. high.   £70

A late Victorian circular tortoise-shell inkstand with plated rococo scroll mounts, on bun feet, London, 1899, 5¼in. **£249**

A late Victorian double ink-stand, by W. J. Barnard, London, 1894, 11in. long. 25oz. **£520**

An Edwardian oblong ink-stand in the Regency taste, W.K., London, 1910, 8½in. long, 17oz. free. **£660**

A rare dark green glass pump-kin inkwell embossed with F. M. & Co. (F. Mordant). **£60**

Aqua glass birdcage inkwell embossed with bars, a door and two feeders. **£25**

Very rare green glass globe inkwell embossed with lines of longitude and latitude as a representation of the world. **£100**

An unusual glass 'Cottage' inkwell. **£30**

A large Lalique moulded glass inkwell. **£1,125**

Green glass cottage inkwell with vertical cavity at the rear to hold a free nib, 6cm. high. **£100**

INKWELLS

A Victorian silver-mounted gadrooned heart-shaped tortoiseshell ink stand with loop handle, William Comyns, London 1889, 4¾in. long. £308

Lalique opaque blue stained glass circular inkwell moulded with four mermaids, 6¼in. diam. £520

A James Powell & Sons green glass inkwell with silver cover, 15cm. diam., 1906. £90

Aqua glass cottage inkwell with stippled roof and no side embossing, 6cm. high. £70

An extremely rare circular cottage inkwell in aqua glass with Registry of Designs diamond embossed on the base for August 1868, 6cm. high. £200

A rare cottage inkwell in aqua glass with Registry of Designs diamond embossed on the front for April 5th 1869, 5½cm. high. £100

Rare cottage inkwell with water butt in green glass embossed C. Chandler & Co., 6cm. high. £100

Aqua glass inkwell in the form of an igloo embossed with tiny blocks and with U.K. Registration Diamond on the base. £120

A cobalt blue glass square shaped inkwell with cavity for free pen nib. £20

INKWELLS

A George III inkstand, by Samuel and George Whitford, London, 1804, 9in. long, 17.75oz. free. £600

Aqua glass cottage inkwell with water butt, bay windows and tiled roof, 6cm. high. £70

Indian chased white metal inkstand with two glass bottles, ivory inlaid border to stand, 10½in. wide. £100

Bonds aqua glass inkwell embossed with Registry of Designs diamond and pen rest, 6cm. high. £30

An aqua glass snail inkwell. £50

A Whitefriar's paperweight inkwell, from the Bacchus period, circa 1840, 7in. high. £281

A Tiffany Studios bronze and glass inkwell, 18cm. diam., stamped Tiffany Studio New York, 69391. £360

Aqua glass umbrella inkwell embossed with G. H. Fletcher, London. £25

An aqua glass tea kettle inkwell. £50

JARS

A large translucent glass jar with thick inverted rim and domed base, Tang/Song Dynasty, 32cm. diam. £6,480

A Daum etched and enamelled glass jar with cover, circa 1900, 8.5cm. high. £440

A cameo glass and ormolu mounted veilleuse, the glass by Emile Galle, 12cm. high. £800

Early 18th century posset jar and cover, 21.5cm. high. £1,540

A pair of 19th century glass specie jars enamelled in white on the inside and enamelled colours with the Royal Arms, 18.1/8in. high. £528

Late 19th century wheel etched and enamelled humidor, Russia, 8¼in. high. £120

Late 19th century Webb ivory cameo rose jar of squat spherical form, 5¾in. high. £885

A 19th century glass drug jar with a lid, 24in. high. £140

A glass jar with pewter cover and mounting, after a design by Peter Behrens, 6¼in. high. £267

A silver and glass fruit-cup jug, by Nicholls & Plincke, in wooden case, circa 1885, 15.3/8in. high.   £5,280

Smith Bros. enamel decorated creamer, Mass., circa 1890, 3.3/8in. high.   £104

An enamelled glass jug with stopper, by Galle, decorated with enamelled hearts and a dwarf playing a violin, 20cm. high.   £440

A Nailsea jug, dark green splashed with white, with flared neck, 23cm. high.   £77

A Wm. Hutton & Son silver and green glass cruet jug, London hallmarks for 1903, 18cm. high, 8oz.14dwt.   £150

An oviform water jug with applied scroll handle, 6½in. high.   £33

A Bohemian dated enamelled jug with applied loop handle 1601, 15cm. high.   £1,980

A French 'turquoise' opaline tapering oviform jug with scroll handle, circa 1835, 16cm. high.   £370

One of two late 17th century Venetian small jugs with applied blue rims, 10cm. high.   £302

JUGS

Late 19th century cameo glass metal mounted jug in cranberry coloured glass.
£400

A small Daum rectangular section cameo glass jug, circa 1900, 11cm. long.
£300

An Elton squat globular jug with elongated spout, 16.5cm. high.
£100

A Venini glass jug in clear glass striped with green, purple and blue, 29.5cm. high, 1950's.
£150

A Galle enamelled glass jug, the ovoid body with faceted neck and angled handle, 1890's, 21cm. high.
£300

Mid 19th century Clichy filigree jug with applied loop handle, 35.6cm. high.
£320

A diamond quilted satin glass creamer, probably England, circa 1880, 3¾in. high.
£174

A 17th/18th century Spanish amethyst jug, 22.5cm. high.
£220

An oviform wrythen-moulded cream jug, 3½in. high. £55

JUGS

A large Schneider mottled glass pitcher, in red glass streaked with yellow, 1920's. £250

Small Daum etched and enamelled glass jug, marked, circa 1900, 7.25 cm. high. £850

A 16th/17th century Spanish serving vessel of green tint, 25.5cm. high. £330

A Bohemian white and clear overlay glass jug, decorated with stylised morning glory and arrowhead foliage, 13in. high. £190

Ravenscroft 'crizzled' decanter jug with tapering oviform body, circa 1685, 23.5 cm. high. £1,000

A Venini glass jug, cylindrical, shaped spout, green glass banded in milky blue, 1950's, 24.5cm. high. £175

An Elton jug with bifurcated spout and handle above, 18cm. high. £270

A green glass Art Nouveau wine jug of slender trumpet form with pewter mounts and handles, 11in. high. £80

A Nailsea jug, pale green, with strap handle, the neck with white enamel rim, 19.5cm. high. £209

LAMPS

An Art Nouveau bronze and leaded glass shade on bronze base, 22½in. high.   £700

A Gabriel Argy-Rousseau pate-de-verre and wrought-iron veilleuse, 17.5cm. high.
£3,080

Early 20th century table lamp with leaded glass shade, 24in. high. £285

Late 19th century pink enamelled satin glass lamp with matching base, 7½in. high.   £130

An Art Nouveau table lamp, beaten brass inset with coloured glass, on oval wooden base, 49cm. high.   £432

Late 19th century Baccarat pressed glass amberina Fairy lamp, France, with cut-out air vents, 4½in. high.   £100

One of a pair of late 19th century pint blown moulded satin glass lamps, France, 8¾in. high.   £70

Art pottery lamp with pierced copper and slag glass shade, circa 1905, 14½in. high. £420

A mid 19th century overlay kerosene lamp, probably Sandwich, 11¾in. high. £410

LAMPS

Early 20th century American bronze and slag glass filigree lamp, 22in. high. £333

Late 19th century Webb decorated Burmese lamp with ruffled base, England, liner signed S. Clarke's Fairy, 5½in. high. £320

A Dufrene polished bronze table lamp with enamelled top, circa 1900, 34cm. high. £132

A Le Verre Francais acid etched table lamp with three-pronged wrought-iron mount, 42.2cm. high. £1,760

An Almaric Walter pate-de-verre and wrought-iron lamp, the amber glass plaque moulded with a blue and amber mottled peacock, 27cm. high. £2,200

A Victorian iron lamp with green tole shaft, stamped Palmer & Co. Patent, 32in. high. £1,404

Late 19th century peach-blow Fairy lamp on three-legged brass stand, possibly Mt. Washington, 8½in. high. £280

A Bradley & Hubbard table lamp with gold iridescent shade, Mass., circa 1910, 15in. high. £416

An Art Nouveau bronze oil lamp base with jewelled glass shade and glass funnel, cast after a model by G. Leleu, circa 1900, 57cm. without funnel. £594

LAMPS

An Art Deco frosted glass lamp painted in colours with banding and linear decoration, 31cm. high. £320

Late 19th century Burmese glass epergne on mirrored plateau, 16in. high. £645

Cameo glass lamp with baluster stem and mushroom shade, circa 1910-20, 41cm. high. £850

An Art Deco figure table lamp in green patinated metal, signed Limousin, 16½in. high. £300

A copper and leaded glass piano lamp, cone-shaped slag glass shade, incised mark 'KK', 13¾in. high. £216

An Andre Delatte cameo table lamp with metal neck mount, 52.5cm. high. £1,650

An Art Deco wrought iron hanging light, attributed to Edgar Brandt, circa 1925, 37cm. high. £400

Late 19th century cranberry blown-moulded two-faced owl-pyramid lamp, 4¼in. high. £50

An Art Deco bronze patinated metal and glass table lamp, signed Vincent 1923, 21in. high. £240

LAMPS

An iridescent glass and electroplated table lamp by Osiris. £486

Late 19th century jewelled cast brass Fairy lamp with clear glass 'wee-fairy' candle cup, 4in. high. £80

Art Nouveau bronzed spelter table lamp, inscribed L. Ock, 38in. high. £570

A 19th century Continental soda glass lace maker's lamp, of baluster form, 22cm. high. £180

A Lalique table lamp, the clear satin finished glass with amber staining, 27.1cm. high. £2,640

Muller Freres cameo glass illuminated column table lamp and mushroom shaped shade, 23in. high. £500

Early 20th century Pairpoint puffy boudoir lamp, Mass., 8in. high. £570

Late 19th century pale pink Parian rose light with clear pressed glass cup, 3¾in. high. £129

Bronze table lamp with green swirl glass and calcite shade, probably Steuben, circa 1910, 14in. high. £524

LAMPS

A Degue Art Deco glass lamp, 35 cm. high. £200

Late 19th century Webb peachblow Fairy lamp in matching base, England, the base having a ruffled and fluted rim, 5½in. high. £445

A bronze lamp in the style of Gustav Gurschner, supporting a Loetz glass shade. £1,250

A Marvin cold-painted metal lamp with Muller Freres cameo glass shade, circa 1905. £800

A bronze, marble and glass lamp cast after a model by M. Le Verrier, signed, circa 1925, 86.2cm. high. £1,404

Late 19th century Webb & Sons Fairy lamp, the plain shade and clear liner fitting into a decorated ruffle, 10in. high. £485

Early 20th century Pairpoint reverse painted table lamp, New Bedford, base signed and numbered 3011, 22¾in. high. £1,041

A Loetz glass and gilt metal table lamp. £4,200

An early 20th century Pairpoint table lamp with blown-out shade, New Bedford, 14in. diam. £958

LAMPS

A Daum Nancy acid etched glass table lamp, France, circa 1900, 14in. high. £1,388

American late 19th century double arm brass student lamp with lithophane shades, 24in. high. £800

Late 19th century lemon yellow camphor striped satin glass Fairy lamp on metal stand, 11.1/8in. high. £120

Late 19th century blue swirled, ruffled satin glass lamp with matching base, 7½in. high. £98

A Gabriel Argy-Rousseau pate-de-verre and wrought-iron veilleuse, the grey, blue and dark blue mottled glass moulded with stylised leaves, 25.5cm. high. £2,200

Iorio dogwood paperweight lamp on opalescent ground, 1981, 5in. high. £40

Late 19th century bisque-fired Christmas tree fairy lamp and clear Cricklite base, Austria and England, 5.1/8in. high. £120

Slag glass and patinated metal table lamp, stamped Sale M Bros., 16½in. high. £142

Late 19th century pink and white end-of-the-day lamp with matching pedestal base, 10.3/8in. high. £120

LAMPS

Bronze and cameo glass
lamp by Loetz, 44cm.
high, circa 1900.
£1,992

A slag glass and gilt metal
table lamp, America, circa
1910, 23½in. high, shade
17¾in. diam.   £142

Cast brass astral lamp
with cut glass shade,
American, circa 1870,
26½in. high.   £315

A Roycroft copper lamp
with Steuben gold irides-
cent glass shade, circa
1910, 16in. high. £1,170

Late 19th century pink
mother-of-pearl satin glass
lamp with matching base
and clear glass candle cups,
6in. high.   £54

Reverse painted and gilt
metal table lamp, by
Bradley & Hubbard, circa
1910, 23¼in. high. £245

A WMF Ikora Art Deco
glass and chrome table
lamp, 18in. high, with
the original seaweed decorated plastic shade.   £65

A 19th century dark blue
tinted lacemaker's lamp,
27cm. high.   £385

Hampshire pottery lamp
with leaded shade, circa
1910, 19½in. high, 16in.
diam.   £524

LAMPS
DAUM

A Daum cameo glass table lamp with conical shade, 51cm. high, signed. £3,000

A Daum cameo table lamp with wrought-iron, three-branch neck mount, 44.1cm. high.   £6,050

A Daum enamelled and acid etched cameo table lamp with three-cornered bulbous domed shade, 45.3cm. high.   £6,264

A Daum overlaid and acid-etched table lamp with wrought-iron mount, 60cm. high.   £7,700

A Daum Art Deco table lamp, frosted glass with wrought iron, engraved with cross of Lorraine, circa 1925, 46cm. high.   £3,240

A Daum enamelled and acid etched landscape table lamp with wrought-iron mounts, 48.5cm. high.   £3,190

GALLE

A Galle cameo glass table lamp with domed shade of amber tone, 57cm. high, signed.   £5,800

A Galle cameo glass lamp shade on Austrian earthenware base, circa 1900, 50cm. high.   £1,540

A Galle glass table lamp with domed shade, 52cm. high, signed in fine linear manner on shade and on base 'Galle'.   £3,800

LAMPS
GALLE

Galle cameo glass domed
top lamp, circa 1900,
52cm. high. £3,035

An Emile Galle glass
lamp, 33cm. high, circa
1900. £4,400

Bronze and ivory lamp base
with Galle cameo glass shade,
circa 1900, 56cm. high.
£1,650

A Galle cameo glass table
lamp with domed shade and
baluster base, 60cm. high.
£7,560

A Galle double overlay cameo
glass lamp, circa 1900, 32.4cm.
high. £7,560

A tall Galle cameo table lamp,
the domed shade and stem
overlaid with claret-coloured
glass, 63.5cm. high. £8,800

A Galle double overlay and
wheel-carved glass table
lamp, the matt-yellow ground
overlaid in brown, blue and
purple, circa 1900, 52.5cm.
high. £6,480

A Galle blowout lamp, varying shades of red on an
amber ground, signed, circa
1900, 44.5cm. high.
£41,040

A Galle triple overlay
cameo glass lamp, blue and
green over a pale amber
ground, circa 1900, 61cm,
high. £9,720

LAMPS
HANDEL

Handel table lamp with glass shade painted and decorated with Persian style border, 22in. high. £1,500

Handel leaded glass table lamp with cone shade, 23½in. high. £1,000

Handel type table lamp, painted and decorated with rust floral design, shade 16in. diam. £333

An early 20th century Handel lamp on Hampshire pottery base, with Mosserine shade, 20in. high. £625

A Handel adjustable desk lamp, with green glass shade, circa 1920, 12¾in. high. £446

Early 20th century Hampshire pottery lamp with leaded Handel shade, 21in. high, 16in. diam. £490

PAIRPOINT

Pairpoint floral and butterfly puffy table lamp, signed, 18in. high. £2,000

Pairpoint reverse painted open top table lamp, signed, 16in. diam. £1,200

Pairpoint puffy rose table lamp with tree trunk base, shade 8in. diam. £630

LAMPS
TIFFANY

Tiffany table lamp with Favrile glass shade, shade 7in. diam.   £1,266

A Tiffany Studios 'lotus' leaded glass and bronze table lamp, 62.5cm. high. £10,450

Tiffany Favrile lamp shade on metal base, signed.   £2,500

A Tiffany Studios bronze and glass filigree table lamp, 42.5cm. high.   £2,530

A Tiffany Studios stained glass dragonfly lamp/pendant, 25.5cm. wide, chain for suspension.   £500

A Tiffany apple blossom table lamp with pierced base.   £17,460

A Tiffany Studio lamp with green-blue Favrile glass shade moulded as a scarab, N.Y., circa 1902, 8½in. high.   £1,875

Bronze Tiffany desk lamp with gold iridescent shade, circa 1920, 19½in. high.   £533

A Tiffany Studios 'Pansy' leaded glass and bronze table lamp, 54cm. high.   £5,500

LAMPS
TIFFANY

Tiffany colonial gold leaded glass table lamp, 22in. high. £2,270

A Louis Comfort Tiffany bronze leaded glass and favrile glass two-light table lamp, 56cm. high. £4,320

A Tiffany Studios 'Dragonfly' leaded glass and gilt bronze table lamp, 46.7cm. high. £17,050

A Tiffany three-light table lamp, the bronze base bun-shaped on four ball feet, 41cm. diam. of shade, 63.5cm. high. £7,560

One of a pair of Tiffany Studios three-light lily, gold favrile glass and bronze table lamps, 33.2cm. high. £4,400

A Tiffany three-light table lamp, shade 40.6cm. diam., 61.5cm. high. £7,560

Early 20th century Tiffany bronze table lamp with leaded shade, 22in. high. £1,748

Early 20th century Tiffany bronze bridge lamp, New York, with a Quezal shade, 54½in. high. £966

Lead Favrile glass and bronze table lamp, by Tiffany Studios, circa 1910, 25¼in. high. £4,300

LANTERNS

American 19th century
tin and glass lantern,
20in. high.   £256

American 19th century
tin and glass lantern
with circular glass win-
dows, 22½in. high.
£256

A 17th century Dutch
ebony lantern with rect-
angular glazed body, 18in.
high.   £842

A brass and glass ship's
lantern, with a plaque
inscribed 'Samuel Hall/Ship
Chandler/East Boston',
mounted as a lamp, 15in. high.
£287

A pair of 19th century, blown,
colourless glass hanging lamps,
approx. 15in. high.   £916

A Regency brass frame
hall lantern with six glass
panels, one a door, 26in.
high.   £1,250

A George III ormolu hall
lantern with arched glazed
cylindrical body, 20in. diam.
£5,184

Early 20th century leaded
cased glass lantern in
vintage pattern, 13¼in.
high, 9in. wide. £315

Late 19th century pink
milk glass lighthouse,
France, 7in. high. £80

LUSTRES

One of a pair of mid 19th century cut-glass lustres, 37.5cm. high. £200

Pair of 19th century opalene crystal candlesticks, 15½in. high. £481

One of a pair of 19th century pink and white overlaid glass lustres, 13½in. high. £150

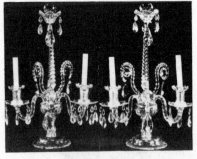

One of a pair of 19th century green and white overlaid glass lustres. £450

A pair of Georgian cut glass double-light candelabra, each with a circular finial over a scalloped cup hung with prisms, 21in. high. £1,663

One of a pair of Bohemian gilt and overlay lustres, circa 1860, 29.5cm. high. £530

One of a pair of Venetian glass table lustres, 38.5cm. high. £550

Pair of 19th century cut glass lustres, 11½in. high. £421

One of a pair of 19th century Bohemian cranberry tinted glass lustres, 12¼in. high. £600

MILK BOTTLES

Matthews Dairy
½ pint, 1970's.
50p

Northern Dairies
sterilized milk
bottle, 1970's.
10p

1980's milk bottle
from Bartonsham
Farm.   10p

Late 19th century
sterilized milk
bottle.   £3

A vase-shaped bottle
by J. W. MacDougall,
Clovenfords, 1930's.
£5

Early 20th century
1 pint 'Special
Milk'.   £2

Early 20th century
1 pint milk bottle.
£2

A late 19th century
Thatcher Milk Pro-
tector.   £150

Late 19th century
swing stopper. £3

123

MINERAL WATER BOTTLES

Connor's Patent (1897). Two bulbous cavities in neck to retain a pear-shaped glass stopper. Codd Patent washer seal, aqua coloured, 9in. high. Embossing, front — Spencer Connor & Co., Manchester; back — Connor's Patent Stoppers, Redfearn Bros. Bottle Makers, Barnsley. £200

Billows Patent (small size). Aqua coloured, cylindrical bottle, with one flat side which has a groove near its base to retain the round glass stopper, Codd-type seal, 7½in. high. Embossing — 'B' Hygienic Registered. £300

Sutcliffe's Patent. Scalloping in shoulders to retain a Sutcliffe & Fewings glass stopper, fitted with a rubber tube, aqua coloured, 8½in. high. Embossing — Cockshott Bros, Trademark (embossed running cockerel), Keighley, Sutcliffe's Patent, Barnsley. £55

A Rylands Patent Codd. Cavity back and front to retain an elongated glass stopper, Codd-type seal, aqua coloured, 9¼in. high. Embossing, front — N. J. Campbell, Foresters Arms, Holyhead; back — Registered No. 448146, Sole Makers, The Rylands Glass And Engineering Co. Ltd., Barnsley. £175

Chapman's Patent Hybrid. Round-ended, aqua coloured bottle with a round rubber ball to close bottle. Two indents in shoulder to retain stopper while pouring, 8½in. high. Embossing, front — Matthew Pomfret Limited Bury, Sykes Macvay & Co. Makers, Castleford; rear — Chapman's Patent Stopper, Birkenhead. £100

Edwards Patent (1874). Flat-bottomed Hamilton, aqua coloured bottle with wired metal cap over a protruding rubber washer, an external annular 'chamber' is formed to retain a round glass marble, 9½in. high. Embossing — Edwards Patent, E. Breffit & Co. Aire & Calder Bottle Works. Very rare. £500

MINERAL WATER BOTTLES

Stone Codd. Brown stone-ware standard Codd shape and seal but both bottle and round marble stopper are made of stoneware, 8½in. high.
Embossing — Cooper's, Mineral Waters, Hanley.
£1,000

J. Lewis Patent. Aqua coloured bottle formed with a double shoulder to retain a long wooden stopper, fitted with a rubber ring, 8½in. high.
Embossing, front — J. Lewis (intertwined initials) Trade Mark, Merthyr; back — J. Lewis's Patent, Merthyr.
£150

Barrett & Elers Hybrid. Round-ended aqua coloured bottle with a long wooden stick stopper fitted with a rubber ring, 9½in. high.
Embossing, front — Virtus Trade Mark; back — Manu-factured by W. Ford, Nottingham.
£150

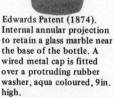

Edwards Patent (1874). Internal annular projection to retain a glass marble near the base of the bottle. A wired metal cap is fitted over a protruding rubber washer, aqua coloured, 9in. high.
Embossing, front — Edwards Patent London, E. Breffit & Co. Makers; rear — London & Castleford.
£80

Aylesbury Patent (1875). The stopper consists of two India-rubber discs on a spindle; the larger one, being the lower, is fixed and the upper disc is free to slide down the rod, aqua coloured, 9¼in. high.
Embossing — Talbot & Co. Trade Mark Registered (embossed entwined initials), Gloucester.
£100

Mitchells Patent (1878). A bulbous cavity at the top of the aqua coloured bottle retains a long glass stopper. Rubber ring on the stopper to seal bottle.
Embossing, front — Mitchell & Mitchell, St. Austell Aera-ted Water Manufacturer, B.B.W. Co. Ltd.; back — As above plus F. B. Mitchell Patentee, St. Austell, Shire Hampton.
£200

MINERAL WATER BOTTLES

Waugh's Patent (1875). Round rubber ball, round shoulders and blob top, deep aqua coloured, 8¾in. high.
Embossing — Waugh's Patent Ball Stopper, Glasgow. £75

Codd's Patent Dumpy (small size), (1872). Round glass stopper, Codd-type seal, dumpy seltzer shaped, aqua coloured bottle, (note narrow neck), 6in. high. Embossing, front — S. Chambers & Co., Henry Street, Bermondsey; back — Codd's Patent, Sole Agents, Barnett & Foster, London, Makers, Rylands & Codd.
£150

Caley's Patent Codd. Standard Codd Patent neck and seal, on a shuttlecock-shaped bottle, aqua coloured, 9in. high.
Embossing, front — Shimmin Sunderland; back — Regd.
£250

Sutcliffe & Fewings Patent (1875). 'The bottle is formed with an internal, annular projection for retaining'. The glass stopper fitted with a rubber tube, dark aqua coloured, 8¼in. high.
Embossing — C. Guest Trade Mark (embossed crown), Barnsley, Sutcliffe & Fewings Patent. £100

Adams & Barrett Patent (1868). A blob topped aqua coloured bottle with double shoulder, closed by a long waisted wooden stopper, fitted with a rubber washer, 7½in. high.
Embossing, front — Fewings & Co. Superior Aerated Waters, Exeter; base — A & B Patent Stopper, Jersey. £75

Edwards Patent (1874). Internal 'chamber' is formed at the base of a Hamilton type bottle, to retain a round glass marble. A wired metal cap is fitted over a protruding rubber washer, aqua coloured, 9½in. high.
Embossing — Edwards Patent, London. Very rare, only two known). £500

MISCELLANEOUS GLASS

Tiffany glass mosaic panel, entitled 'Truth', New York, 1898, 87½ x 44¼in.   £6,665

A clear and frosted glass oval tray with DT monogram mark, for Dorothy Thorpe, 25¼ x 17¾in.   £282

One of three Tiffany iridescent glass scarabs in amber glass, circa 1900, 4.35cm. long.   £120

A Daum limited edition pate-de-verre and fibre glass surrealist sculpture by Salvador Dali, depicting a soft clock slumped on a coat hanger.   £2,052

Two plate glass Royal Warrant Holder's display signs, bearing the coat of arms of H.M. Queen Alexandra, 18½ x 18in.   £275

An Art Deco glass cocktail shaker with silver mounts, Birmingham, 1936, 8in. high.   £400

A cameo glass urn, inscribed Le Verre Francais, 11½in. high.   £495

A jelly glass, the conical bowl engraved with a stag's head and peacock, 3½in. high, circa 1760.   £154

Early 20th century dimpled glass firescreen with an oak frame.   £38

127

MISCELLANEOUS GLASS

A Lalique amber glass
pendant, circa 1925,
4.6cm.   £330

A Schneider etched
smoked glass coupe,
41.5cm., 1920's. £110

A Colin Reid cast glass sculp-
tural form, 37cm. high.
                    £2,200

Exide glass battery case,
8½in. tall.   £2

A Lalique hand mirror, 'Deux
Chevres', 16.20cm. diam., in
original fitted case. £800

A Harden Star fire
grenade in blue
glass.   £30

An English cameo glass
biscuit barrel with plated
mount, swing handle and
cover, 17cm. diam. £700

Two of six 19th century cut
glass stirrup cups, four 6¼in.
high, the other two 7in. high.
                    £322

A Millville steel die sailing boat
mantel ornament, attributed to
Michael Kane, 5½in. high.
                    £691

MISCELLANEOUS GLASS

A 19th century clear and cranberry glass bell, 13in. high, and a red, white and blue Nailsea float, 5in. long. £140

A Lalique etched glass frame with inner border of lilies-of-the valley, 1930's, 33.25cm. £880

A St. Louis crown shot vase, the everted rim with pink and white twisted ribbon border, 3¾in. high. £1,005

Etched glass chalice, signed Marinot, circa 1925, on circular foot, 20.2cm. high. £2,500

A pair of Nancy pate de verre bookends fashioned as dolphins, signed X Momillon, 6½in. high. £2,500

A pipe of opaque white glass, with a waved design in red and blue, 46cm. long. £71

A decalcomania rolling pin, profusely decorated with soldiers, sailors, policemen, female figures and animals, 43.5cm. long. £60

Three of eight Lalique satin glass panels, three rectangular and five of square shape, one panel signed R. Lalique. £1,100

An 'Undene' glass eye cleanser, 3in. tall. £4

PAPERWEIGHTS

Daum pate-de-verre
paperweight modelled
as a moth, signed, 12cm.
wide.   £1.000

A Kaziun poinsettia paperweight, Mass., 2¼in. diam.
          £1,111

A silver and rock crystal
paperweight, St. Peters-
burg, circa 1860, 15cm.
long.   £702

A Kaziun snake paperweight,
Mass., 1940's, signed with gold
K on bottom, 2.5/16in. diam.
          £833

An Almaric Walter pate-de-
verre paperweight, the blue
glass moulded as a bird,
12cm. high. £550

A Gillinder flower weight,
2.7/8in. diam. £534

A French (unknown factory)
strawberry weight, 3.1/8in.
diam.   £2,200

A New England blown pear
weight, 3¼in. diam. £754

A Paul Stankard St. Anthony's
fire spray weight, signed on a
cane with the initial S and engraved script number 39776,
7.6cm. diam. £432

PAPERWEIGHTS

A Bacchus close concentric millefiori weight, 9.2cm. diam. £540

A Lalique presse-papiers in clear and satin-finished glass moulded as a reclining Indian sacred bull, 5.2cm. high. £495

A Mount Washington magnum pink rose weight, 4in. diam. £2,514

A Sandwich blue poinsettia weight, the pale-blue flower with twelve petals, 2½in. diam. £314

A sulphide paperweight, the lobed globular surmount inset with a crystallo-ceramie bust of Voltaire, 12.5cm. diam., possibly reduced. £300

A Mount Washington magnum pink dahlia weight, 4¼in. diam. £16,342

A French scramble paper-weight with blue, green, white and red canes, 3in. diam. £291

A New England blown apple weight, the fruit of bright pink tint, 2½in. diam. £691

Mid 19th century Sandwich cherry paperweight, probably by Nicholas Lutz, 2.15/16in. diam. £489

PAPERWEIGHTS

A Millville rose pedestal weight, the flower with numerous bright yellow petals, 3¾in. high. £754

Charles Kaziun miniature rose weight with pedestal base, Brockton, Mass., 2.1/8in. high. £183

A Millville rose pedestal weight, the flower with numerous dark red petals, 3½in. high. £502

A large Paul Ysart garlanded flat bouquet weight, 9.5cm. diam. £648

A Lalique clear and frosted glass presse-papiers, the plaque intaglio moulded with the figure of St. Christopher carrying the infant Christ, 4½in. high. £440

A Paul Ysart bouquet weight, the centre to one flower with PY initials, 7.6cm. diam. £324

A Paul Ysart garlanded bouquet weight, with PY initials included in the bouquet, 7.5cm. diam. £324

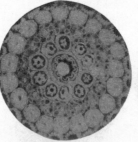

A Bacchus concentric mille-fiori paperweight, the dark green central cane encircled by five rows of canes in red, white and blue, 8.5cm. diam. £450

A Paul Ysart double-fish weight on a translucent amethyst base, signed PY on a cane, 7.5cm. diam. £410

132

PAPERWEIGHTS

A New England apple
paperweight, set on a
circular clear glass base,
7.3cm. diam.£495

Charles Kaziun miniature
millefiori weight with
pedestal base, 2.1/8in.
high. £200

A New England small blown
pear weight, 2¾in. diam. £408

A Kaziun pansy paperweight,
Mass., signed with gold K on
bottom, 2.1/8in. diam. £520

An Almeric Walter pate-de-
verre paperweight designed
by H. Berge, 8cm. high.£9,350

A Kaziun pedestal rose,
Mass., signed with gold K
on bottom, 2in. diam. £347

A Kaziun Morning Glory
paperweight, Mass., 2.1/16in.
diam. £694

A 19th century New Eng-
land Glass Co. apple paperweight, 2½in. high.   £500

A 20th century Charles
Kaziun miniature faceted
weight, Mass., 1¼in. diam.
£990

GLASS

PAPERWEIGHTS
BACCARAT

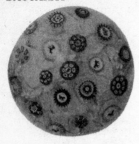

A Baccarat dated scattered millefiori weight, 7.8cm. diam.   £702

Mid 19th century, probably Baccarat, pansy paperweight with star-cut base, 2.5/8in. diam. £185

A Baccarat double-clematis weight on a star-cut base, 6.5cm. diam. £440

A Baccarat faceted marguerite weight, on a star-cut base, 8cm. diam. £6,560

A Baccarat faceted sulphide huntsman paperweight, 8.5cm. diam. £550

A Baccarat pink and white dog-rose weight, on a star-cut base, 6.7cm. diam.   £702

A Baccarat mushroom weight on a star-cut base, 8cm. diam.   £1,728

A Baccarat patterned millefiori white carpet-ground weight, 3in. diam. £3,457

A Baccarat 'thousand-petalled' rose weight, 7cm. diam. £2,420

134

PAPERWEIGHTS
BACCARAT

A Baccarat miniature coloured sulphide pansy weight, 4.7cm. diam. £810

A Baccarat mushroom weight on a star-cut base, 8cm. diam. £550

A Baccarat dated red carpet ground weight, a cane inscribed 'B 1848', 8cm. diam. £3,780

A Baccarat blue and white flower weight on a star-cut base, 6.7cm. diam. £385

A Baccarat garlanded butterfly weight, on a star-cut base, 3.1/8in. diam. £1,382

A Baccarat white double clematis weight, on star-cut base, 6.4cm. diam. £540

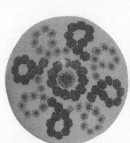

A Baccarat patterned millefiori weight, 7.7cm. diam. £172

A Baccarat blue pompom and bud weight, 3.1/8in. diam. £7,500

A Baccarat close millefiori mushroom weight on a star-cut base, 8cm. diam. £518

PAPERWEIGHTS
BACCARAT

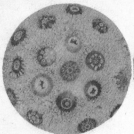

A Baccarat carpet-ground weight, the ground of white corrugated canes with pink centres, 8cm. diam. £2,750

A Baccarat snake weight, 3in. diam. £5,342

A Baccarat carpet-ground weight, dated B1848, 7.3cm. diam. £2,530

A Baccarat flat-bouquet weight with star-cut base, 9cm. diam. £3,850

A Baccarat pale-blue double-overlay mushroom weight on a star-cut base, 3in. diam. £942

A Baccarat yellow and red flower weight, 6.5cm. diam. £1,540

A Baccarat pink clematis-bud weight on a star-cut base, 3¼in. diam. £1,131

A Baccarat garlanded sulphide weight, the crystallo-ceramie portrait of Sir Walter Raleigh in profile, 2¾in. diam. £565

A Baccarat garlanded butter-fly weight, the insect with purple body, blue eyes and marbleised wings, 8cm. diam. £1,540

PAPERWEIGHTS
BACCARAT

A Baccarat garlanded white double clematis weight, on a star-cut base, 7.3cm. diam. £648

A Baccarat close concentric millefiori mushroom weight on a star-cut base, 3.1/8in. diam. £1,068

A Baccarat millefiori initialled weight, the letter A in blue canes, 6.2cm. diam. £702

A Baccarat cobalt ground millefiori paperweight, 3in. diam. £821

A Baccarat paperweight, the flower with a double row of curved petals, pale blue and white, with pale yellow stamens, 5cm. £900

A Baccarat dated close millefiori weight, a cane inscribed 'B 1848', 6.6cm. diam. £648

A Baccarat garlanded butterfly weight, the insect with purple body and turquoise eyes, 7.5cm. diam. £2,385

A Baccarat fruit weight, the clear glass set with a leafy spray bearing two pendant ripe pears, 8cm. diam. £770

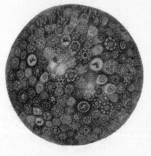

A Baccarat magnum close-millefiori.weight, dated B1848, 10cm. diam. £3,080

PAPERWEIGHTS
BACCARAT

A Baccarat faceted pink-ground sulphide weight, the crystallo-ceramie portrait of St. Joseph, named below, 2.5/8in. diam. £251

A Baccarat garlanded butterfly paperweight, 7.3cm. diam. £715

A Baccarat snake weight, the pink reptile with green spine markings, 7.9cm. diam. £3,300

A Baccarat 'tulip-bud' weight with star-cut base, 8.1cm. diam. £825

A Baccarat faceted concentric millefiori mushroom paper-weight, 7.5cm. diam. £950

A Baccarat mushroom weight with star-cut base, 7.3cm. diam. £648

A Baccarat faceted green-ground sulphide huntsman weight, 3.3/8in. diam. £1,005

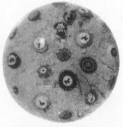

A Baccarat dated scattered millefiori weight, 7.7cm. diam. £715

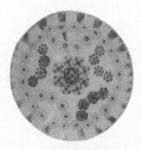

A Baccarat patterned mille-fiori weight, on a sunray-cut base, 7.8cm. diam. £216

PAPERWEIGHTS
BACCARAT

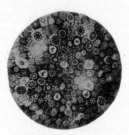

A magnum Baccarat close
millefiori paperweight,
dated 1848, with star-cut
base, 10.2cm. diam. £1,980

A Baccarat flat bouquet
weight, 3in. diam. £7,542

A Baccarat close millefiori
mushroom weight on a
star-cut base, 8cm. diam.
£330

A Baccarat thousand-petal
rose weight, 7.9cm. diam.
£3,740

A Baccarat faceted blue-flash
patterned millefiori weight,
3.1/8in. diam. £1,760

A Baccarat sulphide colour-
ground weight, 8.5cm. diam.
£520

A Baccarat millefiori paperweight, one cane dated B.
1847, 7.5cm. diam. £680

A Baccarat pink-ground
sulphide weight, the sulphide
portrait of Washington,
named on the shoulder, 2¾in.
diam. £754

Á Baccarat bell-flower
weight with star-cut base,
7cm. diam. £4,730

A Clichy colour-ground
weight with opaque-
amethyst ground, 8cm.
£638

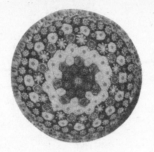

A Clichy close concentric
millefiori weight, 2.7/8in.
diam. £2,011

Clichy swirl weight with
alternate cobalt blue
and white staves, 7.7cm.
diam. £650

A Clichy triple-colour swirl
paperweight, 7.4cm. diam.
£920

Clichy patterned mille-
fiori weight with claret
and white cane, 6.8cm.
diam. £550

A Clichy close millefiori small
paperweight, the canes includ-
ing a pink and a white rose,
5.2cm. diam. £650

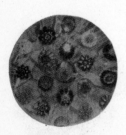

Clichy chequered
concentric millefiori
weight with central
pink rose, 6.7cm. diam.
£625

A Clichy blue-ground concentric millefiori weight, 2.5/8in.
diam. £314

A Clichy colour-ground
weight, the opaque-white
ground studded with
coloured canes, 8.2cm.
£350

PAPERWEIGHTS
CLICHY

A Clichy swirl weight with central green-and-white rose, 5.8cm. diam.   £715

A Clichy flat-bouquet weight, the clear glass set with three sprays bound with a ribbon, 8.5cm. diam.
£10,450

A Clichy initialled 'barber's pole' concentric millefiori weight, 6.8cm. diam. £1,100

Rare Clichy green-ground chequer millefiori weight, 6.4cm.   £500

A Clichy faceted patterned millefiori weight, 3in. diam.
£754

Clichy signed close millefiori weight with brightly coloured canes, 8cm. diam.
£1,600

A Clichy blue ground scattered millefiori weight, 6.5cm. diam. £324

A Clichy flat bouquet weight, 7cm. diam.   £9,720

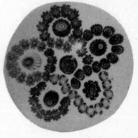

A Clichy garlanded patterned millefiori weight, 7.5cm. diam. £1,188

PAPERWEIGHTS
CLICHY

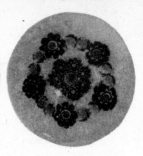

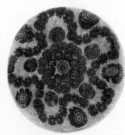

A Clichy faceted patterned concentric millefiori weight, 6.7cm. diam. £486

A Clichy blue double-overlay faceted concentric millefiori mushroom weight on a large star-cut base, 8.3cm. diam. £5,960

A Clichy patterned concentric millefiori weight, 5.5cm. diam. £453

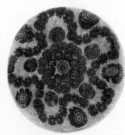

A Clichy moss-ground patterned-millefiori weight, 6.8cm. diam. £4,840

A Clichy swirl weight with central deep pink-and-white cane, 7.9cm. diam. £935

A Clichy patterned millefiori weight, 8cm. diam. £4,530

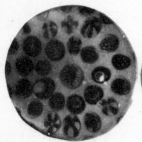

A Clichy 'Sodden Snow' ground concentric spaced millefiori weight, 9cm. diam. £242

A Clichy rose weight, 6.7cm. diam. £4,104

A Clichy blue ground scattered millefiori weight, 8.5cm. diam. £594

PAPERWEIGHTS
CLICHY

A Clichy pink-ground patterned millefiori weight, 8.3cm. diam. £660

A Clichy swirl weight, the alternate pale-pink and white staves radiating from a central large coblat-blue and white cane, 3.1/8in. diam. £880

A Clichy faceted posy weight, on a star-cut base, 6.5cm. diam. £324

A Clichy swirl weight with alternate pink and white staves radiating from a central red, white and green cane, 5.5cm. diam. £528

A Clichy faceted pink double-overlay concentric millefiori mushroom weight on a strawberry-cut base, 3.1/8in. diam. £3,142

A Clichy blue-ground patterned millefiori weight on a translucent cobalt blue ground, 8cm. diam. £440

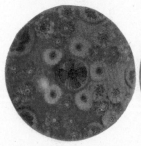

A Clichy green ground patterned millefiori weight, 7.3cm. diam. £594

A Clichy swirl weight with alternate opaque white and turquoise staves, 6.8cm. diam. £594

A Clichy pink and white 'barber's pole' chequer weight, 6.5cm. diam. £1,026

PAPERWEIGHTS
CLICHY

A Clichy garlanded patterned millefiori weight, 7.5cm. diam. £3,780

A Clichy pansy weight, 6.3cm. diam. £972

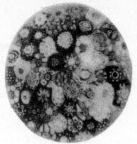

A Clichy miniature close millefiori weight, 4.7cm. diam. £540

A Clichy blue ground patterned millefiori weight, 6.8cm. diam. £453

A Clichy pink-ground patterned concentric millefiori weight, 3.1/8in. diam. £1,382

A Clichy blue and white dahlia weight, 7.2cm. diam. £6,480

A Clichy close millefiori weight, 6.5cm. diam. £810

A Clichy blue and white 'barber's pole' concentric millefiori weight, 6.5cm. diam. £1,188

A Clichy pink ground patterned millefiori weight, 8cm. diam. £594

PAPERWEIGHTS
CLICHY

A Clichy close concentric millefiori weight, 2.1/8in. diam. £2,011

A Clichy swirl weight, with alternate turquoise and white staves radiating from a central claret, green and white cane, 8.2cm. diam. £594

A Clichy flat bouquet weight, 8cm. diam. £22,650

A Clichy convolvulus weight, the clear glass enclosing a white flower with mauve edge, 7.6cm. diam. £4,290

A Clichy 'barber's pole' chequer paperweight, the spaced canes with a central pink rose, 6.8cm. diam. £850

A Clichy red ground concentric millefiori weight, 6.1cm. diam. £410

A Clichy turquoise ground concentric millefiori weight, 6.2cm. diam. £496

A Clichy moss ground flower weight, 6.5cm. diam. £4,536

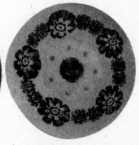

A Clichy patterned concentric millefiori weight, 5.5cm. diam. £345

PAPERWEIGHTS
ST LOUIS

A St. Louis crown weight, 7cm. diam. £540

A St. Louis three dimensional salamander paperweight, 8.6cm. diam. £5,720

A St. Louis crown paperweight, 7cm. diam. £605

A St. Louis blue dahlia weight on a cushion of white spiral latticinio thread, 7.7cm. diam. £638

A St. Louis faceted upright bouquet weight with white torsade, 3in. diam. £2,625

A St. Louis pom-pom weight, the translucent cranberry-red ground set with swirling white threads, 7cm. diam. £940

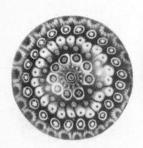

A miniature St. Louis concentric-millefiori weight, 5.2cm. diam. £255

A St. Louis concentric millefiori mushroom paperweight, the base star cut, 7.5cm. diam. £700

A St. Louis small crown weight, 5.5cm. diam. £594

PAPERWEIGHTS
ST LOUIS

St. Louis crown weight with red and blue twisted ribbon, 7.2cm. diam. £1,000

A St. Louis three-dimensional fuschia weight, 7cm. diam. £1,100

St. Louis dated concentric millefiori mushroom weight, on star-cut base, 8cm. diam. £1,250

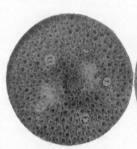

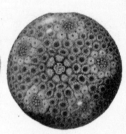

A St. Louis carpet-ground weight, the ground of closely-packed pink crimped canes, 7.5cm. diam. £1,980

A St. Louis faceted upright bouquet weight on a star-cut base, 3.1/8in. diam. £1,445

A St. Louis carpet-ground paperweight, 6.1cm. diam. £2,200

St. Louis pattern fruit glass paperweight on spiralling latticinio basket, 2in. diam. £390

A St. Louis faceted pink clematis paperweight, 7cm. diam. £330

A St. Louis concentric millefiori paperweight, one cane dated SL 1848, 6.8cm. diam. £1,350

PAPERWEIGHTS
ST LOUIS

A St. Louis mushroom weight with star-cut base, 7.3cm. diam.   £1,155

A St. Louis fruit weight, 6.2cm. diam. £432

A St. Louis panelled close millefiori weight, 7.7cm. diam. £3,780

A St. Louis faceted upright bouquet weight, 5.8cm. diam.   £187

A St. Louis faceted upright bouquet weight, 6.5cm. diam.   £935

A St. Louis purple dahlia weight on a star-cut base, 2¾in. diam. £1,634

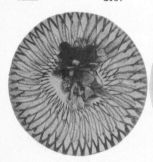

A St. Louis upright bouquet weight, 3in. diam.   £1,508

A St. Louis fuchsia weight, the flower resting on a cushion of white spiral latticinio thread, 8cm. diam.   £1,980

A St. Louis concentric millefiori mushroom weight, on a star-cut base, 7.8cm. diam. £918

148

PAPERWEIGHTS
ST LOUIS

A St. Louis paperweight
with a seven petalled flower
with ribbed pointed leaves,
4.5cm. diam.   £165

A St. Louis four-colour
crown weight, 5.7cm. diam.
                        £600

A St. Louis faceted concentric millefiori mushroom
weight, 8cm. diam. £388

A St. Louis amber flash garlanded sulphide weight, the
portrait of the young Victoria
in profile, 2½in. diam. £817

A St. Louis crown weight,
2¾in. diam. £1,194

A St. Louis aventurine-
ground garlanded dahlia
weight, 3in. diam.
                        £10,730

A St. Louis coloured-ground
pom-pom weight, set on a
pink cushion with swirling
white threads, 6.9cm. diam.
                        £880

A St. Louis miniature daisy
weight, 4.5cm. diam. £648

A St. Louis pink ground
pom-pom weight, 7cm.
diam.   £1,296

St. Louis signed concentric millefiori weight with five circles of canes, 7.8cm. diam. £1,250

A St. Louis signed and dated concentric millefiori mushroom weight, 8cm. diam. £2,860

Rare St. Louis mushroom weight, on star-cut base, 8cm. diam. £3,000

A St. Louis fruit paperweight, the pear with lime-green stalk surrounded by red cherries, 7.8cm. diam. £2,265

A St. Louis fruit paperweight, set with two pears, an apple and four cherries lying on a bed of leaves, 7.8cm. diam. £440

A St. Louis pansy weight with star-cut base, 4.5cm. £255

St. Louis mushroom paperweight in white, blue, pink and green, 7.3cm. diam. £750

A St. Louis concentric millefiori mushroom weight, on a star-cut base, 3.7/8in. diam. £942

St.Louis amber flash posy weight, 6.6cm. diam. £350

PAPERWEIGHTS
ST LOUIS

A St. Louis faceted upright bouquet weight, 2¾in. diam. £1,382

A St. Louis mushroom paperweight with star-cut base. £935

A St. Louis blue dahlia weight, 6.1cm. diam. £864

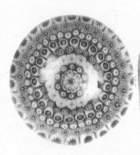

A St. Louis concentric-mille-fiori weight, the central cane surrounded by seven rows of canes in pastel shades, 8cm. diam. £770

A St. Louis faceted blue-berry weight, 2½in. diam. £1,194

A St. Louis blue dahlia weight on a star-cut base, 2¾in. diam. £942

A St. Louis double clematis paperweight, the two rows of pink striated petals with yellow match-head stamen, on a green leafy stalk, 6.4cm. diam. £400

A St. Louis garlanded anemone paperweight, 6.7cm. diam. £605

A St. Louis orange dahlia weight on a star-cut base, 2.11/16in. diam. £11,314

PETROL PUMP GLOBES

Esso petrol pump globe.
£70

Cleveland Super Discol petrol
pump globe.   £100

A National Benzole Mixture,
diamond with Mercury head
petrol pump globe.   £150

A post war B.P. shield petrol
pump globe.   £210

Pratts petrol pump bowl,
pre-war.   £120

A Redline Super, pre war
petrol pump globe. £130

A Shell, first design, pre war
glass petrol pump globe.
£210

Shell petrol pump bowl.
£100

A Pratts post war glass petrol
pump globe.   £300

PITCHERS

Threaded art glass pitcher, tinted in cranberry and amber, circa 1890, 8½in. high. **£157**

Wheeling peach blow drape pattern pitcher, Hobbs, Brockunier & Co., circa 1886, 4½in. high. **£212**

A hand cut crystal tall pitcher with notched handle, circa 1890. **£171**

Late 19th century amberina swirled glass pitcher with angled handle, Massachusetts, 7¼in. high. **£160**

D. Christian cameo glass pitcher, shaped upright pouring lip and applied handle on slender cylindrical form, signature 'D. Christian/Meisenthal/Loth', height 10¼in. **£782**

Late 19th century amberina pitcher with rope handle, 8½in. high. **£200**

PLATES

Libbey cut glass round plate, Toledo, Ohio, circa 1930, 12in. diam. **£600**

A Kosta etched cameo glass plate of frosted grey glass overlaid with amber and dark brown, 1950's, 34.75cm. diam. **£125**

A cameo glass plate engraved by Thomas and George Woodall. **£14,000**

POISON BOTTLES

Poisons, large and small, bottles range in size from 1 dram (bottle third from right) to 40oz. (large centre bottle).

Six sided bottles in green, amber and blue with various embossing. The large bottle on the right is embossed 'Birmingham Workhouse'. Valued between £3 and £15

Cobalt blue six sided poisons, Po/is/on and embossed arrow on rear three panels, all the other panels vertical ribbed, some with ground in blue glass stoppers. £10 to £20 depending on size.

POISON BOTTLES

A mixture of six sided and square bodied poison bottles known as Admiralty. The front panel with an embossed arrow, capacity and the letter N, the remainder being vertical ribbed. These bottles range in size from 1oz. up to 24oz. Value £10 to £40 according to bottle and type.

The two green bottles on the left are embossed 'Maorix' and 'Not To Be Taken', both are rare. Value up to £30.
The cobalt blue bottles on the right are embossed 'Owbridges Embrocation' and 'Owbridges Embrocation Hull'. Value £5 to £10

The bottle in the centre is embossed 'Poison' at the top and bottom of front panel, and 'Public Health Department, Rochdale Corporation', cobalt blue, extremly rare. Value £25. Flanking bottles are cobalt blue and emerald green embossed 'Poison' at the top and bottom of front panel, and 'This bottle is the property of the Sheffield Corporation'. Value £40.

POISON BOTTLES

Known as 'Star' poison bottles (star shaped cross section), they are embossed 'Not To Be Taken' and 'Poison' in the two front panel depressions and Reg. No. 716057 embossed at the foot of the back panel. The bottles range from 1oz. to 16oz., are cobalt blue, green and amber glass with wide and narrow mouth types. Value ranging between £35 to £70, cobalt blue bottles command higher prices.

Known as 'Crescent' poison bottles, Registered in 1905, (crescent shaped in cross section) they have 'Not To Be Taken' down front panel or, and much rarer, 'Poison'. Found in cobalt blue, copper blue, emerald green, and aqua glass. Value £10 to £20

Wilsons Patent emerald green, triangular bottles with notched edges and 'Not To Be Taken' and 'Patent' on the left front panel, 'Caution' and sometimes 'Parkes Drug Stores' on the right, Patented in 1899, sizes range from ½oz. to 24oz. Value £45 to £75 depending on size.

POISON BOTTLES

Taylors Liverpool Patent, emerald green bottles have three flat sides and a curved back, with embossed 'Caution' at top of rear panel, Reg. No. 409210 at the foot and 'Not To Be Taken' down front panel. The base is embossed 'Taylor Liverpool' and with capacity. Patented 1905 - they have rows of bumps on the front panels. Value £15 to £40 depending on size. (Very small and large sizes in most Patents are often the rarest and are worth more.)

Four Ammonia Poisons in shades of green and brown. Bottle second from right is of rare triangular shape, is embossed with 'Sharpes Ammonia' and 'Not To Be Taken'. Value £50. Other bottles £5 to £15.

Three shaped Poisons — left, triangular shape with curved back, 'Not To Be Taken' down front and vertical ribbing on adjacent panels, shades of green and black. Value £5.
Middle — 'Carbolic Acid Poison' on front panel, this bottle is rectangular shaped in amber glass. Rare £25.
Right — cobalt blue bottle with 'Poison' at the foot of the front panel, 'Ossidine' on the left and 'Coles Patent England' on the right panel. Very rare, only three known. Value £70 plus.

Ammonia Poisons, three identical bottles, from left in amber, green and cobalt glass, embossed 'Ammonia' across top and 'Caution', 'Poisonous', 'Not To Be Taken' down front panel. Value £10 to £25 depending on colours.

Three rare Poisons in cobalt blue glass — left, Tippers Poison bottle which tapers from shoulder to base and has 'Poison' embossed across the top of the front, 'Tippers Animal Medicines' at foot, Patented 1904. Value £100 plus.
The middle bottle has 'Poison' on the shoulder, rows of diamond points on the sides, and the base has 'Patent' embossed on the rim, and L. and T. Co. embossed in the centre. Value £75.
The bottle on the right is American, known as 'Quilt Poison', has cross hatching around the sides of the bottle and has a stopper with sharp points and embossed 'Poison' at side and top. Value £100

Lysol Disinfectant bottles in a range of sizes with various embossings, in blue, green, amber and black glass. Value 50p to £10. Black and blue being much rarer.

Three stoneware Poisons with the outer bottles stamped 'Poison', 'Royal Infirmary
Manchester'. Value £10 to £15.

Poison bottles with skulls — the three larger bottles illustrated are all emerald green, of
German origin, and have embossed skull and cross bones and also embossed 'Gift Flasche'
which translated indicates 'Poison Bottle'.
The bottle second from left is of American origin, is coffin shaped and has a skull and
cross bones embossed on front with the rear embossed R.I.P.   £125

Skull Poisons, Patented by Carlton H. Lee, 1894, in America, are rare and come in three
sizes of cobalt blue glass. Value £350 plus.

POISON BOTTLES

Quine's Patent, aqua glass bottle with 'Poison' embossed on the side or back, and capacity embossed on belly, Patented 1893. Various sizes exist, all rare. £75 plus.

Martins Patent bottle 1902. The bottle stands as shown, the U bend is believed to act as a trap to prevent spilling the contents. Various sizes and embossings exist with the rare types having 'Poison', 'Not To Be Taken' embossed on side, with others just 'Poison', also embossed 'The Martin Poison Bottle'. Can be found in aqua and ice blue glass and are thought to exist in amber and cobalt blue. For very small and large sizes prices increase £75 up to £150.

Submarine Poison Design Reg. 1899. (Not granted Patent until 1906). There are three sizes known all in cobalt blue with 'Poison' embossed on one side and Reg. No. 336907 on the base. Rare in all sizes and highly sought after by collectors. £100 — £150 depending on size.

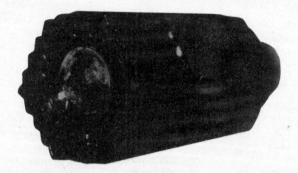

This illustration shows the base view of a six sided poison bottle in cobalt blue, embossed with Savory's Patent and bearing a Pontil mark. It was patented by John Savory and William Barker in January 1859 and from this patent all forms of six sided poison bottles evolved. This particular bottle, with the base embossing and Pontil mark, is the only one known to exist and could be valued up to £500.

O'Reilly's Patent, known as Binoculars Poison. Bottle is ice blue, has 'Poison' across shoulder and embossed on cylinder bottom sections, and is also embossed on the base 'O'Reillys Patent 1905'. Only two of these bottles are known, the other bottle is in an American collection. £800 plus

Very rare 'Wasp Waist' Poison, of which various sizes exist, with rows of diamond points embossed on the front and side panels and the Reg. No. 460944 at the foot of the back panel, cobalt blue only, Patented 1894. £450 plus

'QUACK' MEDICINE AND 'CURE ALL' BOTTLES

J. Cropper's 'Never Failing Gout Mixture', in aqua coloured glass bottle, circa 1850.   £20

Pre 1850 Ruspinis Styptic in cobalt blue pontilled bottle.   £100

Dalby's Carminative, in a cone-shaped aqua bottle.   £30

Large size, clear glass Congreaves Balsamic Elixir for (W)Looping Cough and Asthma.   £30

Cordial Balm of Syriacum, in aqua glass bottle.   £100

Henry's Calcined Magnesia, Manchester, in a lead glass pontilled bottle.   £30

Dr. Solomon's Cordial Balm of Gilead, in moulded aqua glass bottle.   £150

Dr. McMunn's Elixir of Opium, in aqua glass pontilled bottle.   £40

'By the King's Patent', True Cephalic Snuff, in a crudely blown pontilled bottle of light green glass.   £100

'QUACK' MEDICINE AND 'CURE ALL' BOTTLES

Dr. Wartburg's Fever Tincture, Tonic Medicine, in aqua moulded bottle.   £50

Violin shaped clear glass pontilled bottle, 'By the King's Patent Granted to Robt. Turlington — For His Invented Balsam of Life — Jan. 26th 1754.   £100

Holden's 'Tommy' bottle, 7½ pence size, Cures Sprains and Sore Throats, aqua glass.   £30

Holden's 'Tommy' bottle, 13½ pence size, Cure for Sprains, Bruises, Rheumatism, Sore Throats and Sciatica, rare aqua glass. £40

True Daffys Elixir, in a lime green pontilled bottle. £100

George Handyside's 'Rheumatic Cure', in clear glass, rare.   £30

'Yours truly' cures pains, rheumatism, Sheffield, rare aqua glass.   £30

Miss Pikes Powders for Fits and Nervous Complaints, in a lead glass bottle, circa 1800.   £100

Dr. Lobb's Blob Lipped, cylindrical clear glass bottle. with an embossed humanoid face on the reverse.   £140

'QUACK' MEDICINE AND 'CURE ALL' BOTTLES

George Handyside's 'Blood Purifier', in black glass, rare. £80

Edgar's Group Lotion, 'The Children's Life Preserver', in octagonal aqua glass bottle. £30

George Handyside's small 'Blood Food' in black glass full of attractive yellow bubbles, rare. £50

William Radam's Microbe Killer, a beautifully embossed rare amber glass bottle. £80

A rare, large size, copper blue Clarke's 'World Famed Blood Mixture'. £35

Dr. Hasting's Naphtha Syrup in rectangular shaped aqua glass pontilled bottle. £80

GLASS

ROEMERS

A Netherlands or Rhenish roemer, the egg-shaped bowl and hollow stem applied with irregular prunts, 15.5cm. high.   £160

German 17th/18th century armorial roemer with wide shallow cup-shaped bowl, 20.5cm.
£1,100

Late 17th century Netherlands green tinted roemer, the stem applied with raspberry prunts, 15cm. high.   £715

RUMMERS

A large Sunderland rummer with bucket bowl, circa 1800, 21cm. high.   £800

An Absolon rummer of emerald-green tint, the ovoid bowl decorated in gilt with a sailing ship heightened in black, circa 1800, 12cm. high.
£506

A Sunderland rummer with bucket bowl, on a spreading stem and square lemon-squeezer base, circa 1800, 14cm. high.   £240

SCENT ATOMISERS

A Galle cameo glass perfume atomiser of flattened bulbous shape, circa 1900, 22.3cm. high.   £720

Victorian cut glass scent spray of tear drop design.
£40

Amber and white moulded glass scent bottle, circa 1920.   £12

165

GLASS

SCENT BOTTLES

A cameo scent-bottle and stopper of tapering form with waisted neck, circa 1880, 14.5cm. high. £500

A cameo citrine-ground silver mounted scent bottle, the silver with maker's mark JNM, London, 1884, 14.5cm. long. £264

A Heath & Middleton silver topped glass flask, possibly designed by C. Dresser, Birmingham 1891, 10in. £480

A bottle-shaped cut crystal perfume bottle and matching stopper, with silver spoon and silver rim, hallmarked Sheffield, 1912, 4in. high. £32

19th century cameo glass salts bottle with silver screw top, in case, 4in. long. £195

A St. Louis scent bottle and stopper, set on a paperweight base, 15.1cm. £715

Violette De Parme scent bottle with original label, circa 1920's. £10

A Victorian cut glass heart-shaped double scent bottle, by S. Mordan & Co.,bearing the registered design mark for 1869, 3.1/8in. high. £600

A cameo silver gilt mounted scent bottle and screw cover, maker's mark for Sampson Mordan, London, 1884, 15cm. long. £198

SCENT BOTTLES

A 19th century overlaid cranberry glass scent bottle and stopper decorated with a painted oval portrait of a lady, 5¾in. high. £125

A New England scent bottle and stopper, terminating in a concentric millefiori weight, 21.6cm. £330

Art Deco ruby and diamond scent bottle, by Cartier, Paris. £2,000

A Marinot scent bottle and stopper, with enamel painted decoration, circa 1920, 17cm. high. £1,188

Antique cased set of three scent bottles with ormolu mounts and painted porcelain stoppers. £160

A Clichy cut glass and patterned millefiori scent bottle and stopper, 18cm. high. £1,080

A late Victorian cut glass square cologne bottle with a silver openwork mount by William Comyns, 5½in. high. £385

An opaque scent bottle of flattened pear shape, one side inscribed A*B 1780, Newcastle-upon-Tyne, 7.5cm. long. £352

'Susanna och gubbarna', an Orrefors clear glass decanter and stopper designed by Edvard Hald, circa 1935, 23.5cm. high. £370

SCENT BOTTLES

Late 19th century black and white cameo scent bottle with silver screw cap, 8cm. high. £220

Yardley lavender bottle with original label. £10

Cut glass scent bottle in gold mounted shagreen case, circa 1790, 8.5cm. high. £500

A Baccarat enamelled cut glass scent bottle with gilt metal screw cover, 9.5cm. long. £864

Mid 18th century Venetian enamelled small scent flask from the atelier of O. Brussa, 11cm. high. £1,540

Mid 18th century Venetian lattimo scent bottle of flattened tear-drop form, 10cm. high. £330

Jade glass ovoid perfume flask and stopper, the moulded body decorated with fish, 7in. high. £210

A cameo glass scent bottle in yellow overlaid in ruby, with silver cap, marked Birmingham, 1904, 16cm. £352

A French 'Gorge De Pigeon' opaline flared cylindrical scent bottle and stopper, circa 1835, 11.5cm. high. £300

SCENT BOTTLES

One of a pair of French opaline scent bottles, circa 1840, 12cm. high.
£550.

An enamelled gold and rock crystal scent flacon, St. Petersburg, late 19th century, 4.8cm. high.
£972

Green cut to clear glass cologne bottle, circa 1890, 7¾in. high. £425

An Orrefors perfume bottle and stopper, designed by E. Hald, engraved H 193 24 B9, 15cm. high. £440

An opaque scent bottle of pear shape, one side inscribed I*E:CAY, Newcastle-upon-Tyne, circa 1785, 8.5cm. long.
£110

A crystal perfume bottle/ink well with matching stopper, 3.5in. high. £15

One of a pair of Hawkes stoppered cologne bottles, circa 1890, 6in. high.£400

Coralene decorated perfume bottle with matching beaded stopper, height 6¾in. £139

Late 19th century ivory cameo scent bottle of shouldered form, 5.7cm. £99

A Faberge enamelled and gold-mounted bloodstone perfume flacon, St. Petersburg, 1899-1908, 9cm. high.   £7,020

Late 18th century Spanish opaque opaline scent flask, in the form of a bird, painted in colours and enriched in gilding with flower sprays, 20cm. wide.   £756

Lily of the Valley by Blondeau & Co. Ltd., with original pictorial label, 1920's.   £10

A London or South Staffordshire scent bottle moulded as The Tyrolean Dancers, circa 1770, 3½in. high.   £1,155

A glass scent bottle and stopper, inscribed 'Cigalia, Roger et Gallet, Paris', 13cm. high, in original box.   £280

A Franchini silver gilt mounted millefiori scent bottle, the base with a cane dated 1847, 7.2cm. long.   £270

Cut glass scent bottle with plated top, circa 1920.   £40

French 19th century glass scent casket containing six square bottles and stoppers, 15.5cm.   £400

Dubarry figurines complete with original scent bottle, circa 1930. £15

SCENT BOTTLES

A ruby and white cameo glass scent bottle of teardrop form, with hinged silver cap, marked Birmingham, 1884, 8.7 cm. £500

An English cameo scent bottle, in the form of a swan's head, marked Birmingham 1888, 16cm. £1,050

A 19th century French Art Nouveau glass scent phial with plated mount. £60

A Franchini gilt metal mounted scent bottle, the hinged cover with ring and bead chain attachment, 7.5cm. long. £259

A plain glass atomiser with plated top, circa 1910. £30

Scent casket lined with red silk, circa 1900. £40

Continental amber glass, shaped perfume bottle with matching stopper, 6in. high. £15

A large Yardley scent decanter with stopper. £12

A Schiaparelli scent bottle complete with the original leather case, 1930's. £50

SCENT BOTTLES
APSLEY PELLATT

Cut glass sulphide scent bottle and stopper, Apsley Pellatt, circa 1820, 12cm. high. £420

An Apsley Pellatt cut-glass sulphide scent bottle and stopper, 5.3/8in. high.
£628

An Apsley Pellatt emerald green cut glass scent bottle and stopper, circa 1825, 14cm. high. £220

BOHEMIAN

A Bohemian alabaster glass enamelled and gilt scent bottle, circa 1840, 17cm. £286

Bohemian 'Zwischengold' scent bottle of fluted conical form, circa 1735, 9cm. high. £450

A Bohemian lithyaline scent bottle and stopper, Egermann workshop, circa 1840, 12.5cm. high. £200

DAUM

Daum Nancy perfume bottle, straight diamond shaped bottle, circa 1900, 4½in. high. £200

Unusual Daum cameo glass perfume bottle and stopper, signed, 13.5cm. high.
£425

Daum Cameo and enamelled glass perfume bottle with conforming stopper, signature 'Daum/Nancy', height 4½in. £782

SCENT BOTTLES
GALLE

Galle enamelled glass
perfume bottle and
stopper, signed, 1880's,
10cm. high.   £530

Galle cameo glass perfume
bottle and mushroom stopper,
4½in. wide, 3¾in. high.   £440

A Galle flask-shaped scent
bottle, the neck with a gilt
band, rim chip, 12.5cm.
high.   £396

GILES, JAMES

A gilt decorated blue scent
bottle and stopper, decoration in the atelier of
James Giles, circa 1765, 18cm
high.   £900

A facet cut green scent bottle,
stopper and gold screw cover,
gilt in the atelier of James
Giles, circa 1765, 6cm. long.
                        £935

An opaque white scent bottle
of tear-drop form, gilt in the
atelier of James Giles, circa
1770, 8cm. long.   £462

KAZIUN

Mid 20th century Kaziun
paperweight perfume
bottle, Brockton, Massa-
chusetts, 3½in. high.
                        £300

Mid 20th century Kaziun
paperweight perfume
bottle, Brockton, Massa-
chusetts, 2in. high. £250

Kaziun paperweight per-
fume bottle, circa 1940,
Brockton, Massachusetts,
3½in. high.   £700

SCENT BOTTLES
LALIQUE

A Lalique glass perfume bottle with conical stopper moulded with flowering brambles. £150

'Rosace Figurines', a Lalique frosted glass circular scent flask and stopper, 11cm. high. £400

A Lalique glass perfume bottle and stopper for Worth's 'Dans La Nuit', 1920's. £240

A Lalique perfume bottle decorated with female figures in Greek costume, 15.5cm. high, circa 1925. £350

A set of three Lalique glass perfume bottles in leather carrying case, 1920's, 8.75cm. high. £790

A Lalique glass perfume bottle of rectangular shape with stepped recessed panels, 18.5cm. high. £200

A Lalique glass perfume bottle for Molinard, with spherical stopper, 1930's. £300

A Lalique scent bottle and stopper, the clear glass impressed and moulded with stylised marguerites, 13.2cm. high. £198

A Lalique glass perfume bottle of flattened circular form with spherical stopper, 1930's, 22cm. high. £200

SCENT BOTTLES
LALIQUE

'Worth', a Lalique glass scent bottle, with original Worth paper label, 24.5cm. high.
£280

A Lalique glass perfume bottle, flattened, square body with central oval depression, 1930's, 12.75cm. high. £300

One of a pair of Lalique glass perfume bottles, moulded as sea urchins, 9.5cm. high, 1930's. £150

WEBB

Late 19th century cameo glass scent bottle, by D. & L. Pearce at Thos. Webb & Sons, 5.7cm.
£308

A Webb cameo glass scent phial with Tiffany white metal hinged cap, 6½in. high. £418

A ruby-ground cameo scent bottle with silver mount, Thos. Webb & Sons, circa 1885, the silver London, 1886-87, 11cm. high.
£380

Thomas Webb ruby-ground cameo scent flask with silver screw cover, circa 1888, 14.5cm. high. £600

A Webb ivory cameo glass scent bottle of globular form, marked London 1902. £385

Webb blue-ground cameo scent bottle with hinged silver cover, 1885-87, 10.5cm. high £410

175

SERVING BOTTLES

A 17th century Nether-
landish bottle of amethyst
tint, 21cm. high. £1,100

A 17th century amber-
tinted serving bottle of
depressed globular form,
Netherlandish or Rhenish,
16.6cm. high.   £495

An 18th century Jaco-
bite serving bottle with
beaded knob stopper,
28cm. high.   £1,350

A Galle oviform clear and
enamelled glass bottle decanter
with moulded flutes, 7¾in.
high.   £180

An early serving bottle, the
compressed globular body
with a kick-in base,
circa 1700, 14.5cm. high.
                    £850

A Galle enamelled glass bottle
of flattened flask shape with
stopper, 30.25cm. high.
                    £330

A Nuremburg metal mounted
engraved serving bottle, circa
1700, 27.5cm. high.   £880

Mid 17th century Netherlands
turquoise serving bottle with
gilt metal domed cover, chain
and collar attachment, 18.5cm.
high.   £2,750

A late 17th century Netherlandish blue serving bottle,
17cm. high.   £1,296

SERVING BOTTLES

Late 17th century Netherlandish blue serving bottle with a scroll handle, 13cm. high. £1,620

A 17th century Facon de Venise serving bottle of globular straw-coloured seeded metal, probably Spanish, 25cm. high. £352

A 17th century Netherlandish serving bottle of amethyst tint, with applied loop handle, 17cm. high. £1,760

A Nuremburg engraved serving bottle, the neck with foliate and scrolling floral foliage bands, circa 1700, 25cm. high. £858

A Netherlands diamond engraved, pewter mounted, green tinted serving bottle, inscribed B. Boers, Warmont, 12 April 1690, 25cm. high. £2,750

Mid 17th century Netherlands turquoise serving bottle, the globular body with kick-in base, 19.5cm. high. £2,420

A serving bottle with lightly moulded panelled cylindrical body, early 18th century, 20.5cm. high. £162

An early 18th century clear glass serving bottle and stopper, 11in. high. £410

A 17th century Facon-de-Venise bottle in vetro a fili, 30.5cm. high. £193

SHADES

A Lalique amber glass
hanging shade, 1930's,
30.5cm. diam. £265

Saint-Vincent, a Lalique
amber plafonnier, the circular bowl in clear and satin-
finished glass moulded with
bands of scrolling fruit laden
vines, 34.6cm. wide. £550

A Lalique amber glass
hanging shade, 1920's.
£390

A Le Verre Francais cameo
glass hanging lamp shade in
the form of a strawberry
overlaid in orange and blue,
30.9cm. high. £810

A Lalique opalescent glass
hanging shade moulded with
swags of fruit, circa 1930,
31cm. diam. £275

An American leaded glass
chandelier, 62cm. diam.
£280

A Galle cameo glass shade,
circa 1900, 49.5cm. diam.,
with chains. £990

One of a pair of Daum glass
and metal wall lights, fitted
for electricity, circa 1925,
60cm. wide. £2,050

A pendant lamp shade of
shallow bowl shape, signed
'Maxonade Paris', 1ft.6in.
diam. £190

A Lalique plafonnier, the hemispherical bowl of yellow frosted glass moulded with peaches and leaves, 38cm. wide. £770

Two of a set of four early 20th century leaded glass wall lights, 5½in. high. £3,600

A Lalique amber glass shade, 1920's, 30cm. diam. £340

A Tiffany Studios leaded glass shade, inset with a floral design in deep blue and mauve glass, circa 1900, 46cm. diam. £3,000

An iridescent and leaded glass hanging shade attributed to Tiffany Glass & Decorating Co., circa 1895. £2,380

A cameo glass hanging shade, attributed to Loetz, the mottled pink/white body overlaid in deep red, circa 1900/10, 40cm. max. width. £290

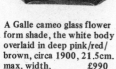

A Galle cameo glass flower form shade, the white body overlaid in deep pink/red/brown, circa 1900, 21.5cm. max. width. £990

A large Daum cameo glass hanging lampshade of shallow domed form, 46cm. diam., signed. £2,100

One of a set of four Tiffany Favrile electric light shades, N.Y., circa 1920, 3½in. high, 4¾in. diam. £350

SNUFF BOTTLES

An 18th century glass overlay snuff bottle with 'snowflake' ground carved in red with chilong. £125

An 18th century glass snuff bottle of spherical shape, probably Beijing workshops. £1,650

An inside painted glass rounded square snuff bottle with jade stopper. £500

Late 18th/early 19th century pink glass snuff bottle, the rim with jewel festoons. £7,150

An inside painted glass rounded square snuff bottle painted with a leopard beneath bamboo, signed Wang Bai-chuan. £248

A Beijing four-colour overlay white-ground spade-shaped snuff bottle carved with dense flowering peony sprays. £280

A mottled glass snuff bottle of ovoid form, mid Qing Dynasty. £385

A six-colour glass overlay snuff bottle with 'snowflake' ground, 1820-80. £3,960

A green overlay caramel-ground disc-shaped bottle carved with figures on terraces, with stopper. £432

A five-colour overlay glass disc snuff bottle with glass stopper.
£378

A glass overlay snuff bottle, with 'snow-flake' ground and a red stork and deer to reverse. £175

A glass overlay snuff bottle with 'snow-flake ground carved in red, dated 1750-1830. £100

Late 18th/early 19th century glass overlay snuff bottle of flattened spherical form.
£528

A glass overlay seal-type snuff bottle of ovoid shape, Yangzhou School.
£2,200

Late 18th/early 19th century glass overlay snuff bottle, the oviform body with a bubble-glass ground with blue overlay. £1,100

An inside painted rock crystal rounded rectangular snuff bottle with figures on a snowy terrace, inscribed, with stopper. £151

An 18th century carved Peking glass snuff bottle of transparent ruby-red metal well carved in high relief. £484

An inside painted glass disc-shaped snuff bottle, dated 1981. £205

GLASS

An inside-painted glass
bottle by Ma Shaoxuan,
dated 1911, depicting
the infant Xuandong
Emperor.　£5,000

Late 18th/early 19th century
snuff bottle, the snowstorm
ground with red overlay.
£825

A two-colour glass overlay
seal-type snuff bottle of
baluster form, Yangzhou
School.　£495

A two-colour glass overlay
snuff bottle, the opaque
white ground with black
and caramel overlay.
£1,100

A glass overlay snuff bottle,
the opaque blue ground
with pink overlay, mid
Qing Dynasty.　£1,375

An inside-painted and carved
rock crystal snuff bottle,
signed Ye Zhongsan and
dated 1933.　£715

A 19th century nine-colour
glass overlay snuff bottle.
£330

A glass inside-painted snuff
bottle, by Shi Chuan, signed, well painted with a
Manchu warrior.　£330

An inside-painted glass snuff
bottle, by Zhou Leyuan,
signed and dated mid Autumn
1890.　£3,300

SNUFF BOTTLES

Late 19th century cameo glass scent bottle by D. & L. Pearce at Thos. Webb & Sons, 6cm.   £330

An inside painted rock crystal rounded rectangular snuff bottle, dated 1919, with blue glass stopper.   £194

An 18th century glass overlay snuff bottle with clear bubble-suffused ground.   £2,090

An inside painted glass rectangular bottle with two equestrian archers pursuing a deer, signed Chen Zhongsan.   £280

A glass overlay snuff bottle, the bubble-suffused ground decorated in green with fruiting pods and gourds, 1800-50.   £120

An inside-painted rock crystal snuff bottle with flaring sides by Ye Zhongsan, signed and dated 1916.   £1,650

A five-colour overlay glass disc snuff bottle with glass stopper.   £500

An inside-painted glass portrait snuff bottle, by Ma Shaoxuan, signed and dated Winter 1909.   £11,000

Late 18th/early 19th century glass overlay snuff bottle, the dense snowstorm ground with blue overlay.   £275

STAINED GLASS

Flemish 16th century
grisaille and yellow-
stained glass roundel,
8½in. diam.   £400

A 16th century circular
stained leaded glass panel
depicting a scene of a
christening, 33.5cm. diam.
£250

Swiss mid 17th century
and later leaded glass
window, 19 x 13.5/8in.
£600

A large 19th century English
stained glass panel showing a
lady in Renaissance costume
at the prie-dieu, 100 x 55cm.
£495

A 17th century French rectangular stained glass panel
centered with an oval of the
martyrdom of St. Stephen,
46.5 x 59cm.   £550

A large rectangular glass panel
by John Hutton, sand blasted
and wheel engraved with
Perseus before the Three Graces,
206.5 x 97cm.   £1,650

Early 16th century Swiss
stained glass armorial
panel, circle of Lukas
Zeiner, 14 x 11in. £1,500

One of a pair of 18th century
English oval stained glass
armorial panels, 46 x 34.5cm.
£440

Early 17th century Swiss
stained glass panel, 17½in.
high, slightly damaged.
£700

STAINED GLASS

A Swiss stained glass panel, painted with scenes from the Story of Joseph, 1554, 12¾ x 9in. £1,210

Flemish 16th century grisaille and yellow-stained roundel of St. Catherine, 8½in. diam. £700

Early 16th century Swiss stained glass armorial panel, 14 x 11in. £2,000

Early 19th century pair of glass paintings, each of a courtier and courtesan, 16.5 x 13.5cm. £750

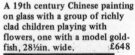

A 19th century Chinese painting on glass with a group of richly clad children playing with flowers, one with a model goldfish, 28½in. wide. £648

One of a pair of early 20th century prairie school-style leaded glass windows, 58in. high, 18in. wide. £262

A 16th century Flemish stained glass panel of the parable of Dives and Lazarus, 23.5 x 17.5cm. £715

A late 19th century leaded stained and coloured glass window, signed W. J. McPherson, Tremont St., Boston, Mass. £490

Swiss stained glass armorial panel, in 16th century style, 13¾ x 9¾in. £350

STAINED GLASS

Swiss stained glass armorial panel in 16th century style, 14½ x 9¾in.   £350

Late 16th century Flemish grisaille and yellow-stained glass roundel of a processional scene, 8½in. diam.   £500

Swiss stained glass panel painted with two men, circa 1600, 17¼in. high.
£650

One of two early 20th century prairie school-style leaded glass windows, 20½ x 53½in., and five smaller, 18 x 18¾in.   £769

An Art Deco leaded stained glass panel by Jacques Gruber, 70.2cm. wide, 50.3cm. high.   £3,520

A large 19th century English stained glass panel of Mary Queen of Scots, 151 x 80cm.
£1,100

One of a pair of 17th century Upper Rhenish stained glass panels, 11¼ x 8½in. £1,250

Flemish 16th century grisaille and yellow-stained glass roundel, 9.5/8in. square. £1,250

A Swiss stained glass armorial panel, 12½ x 9in., 1602.   £800

STAINED GLASS

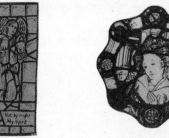

A circular stained glass panel, painted with the head and shoulders of a young girl, circa 1880, 26.8cm. £100

One of a set of four late 19th century stained glass panels, 16¼in. wide. £350

German 16th century leaded stained glass rosette, 15½in. diam. £450

Late Victorian stained glass panel, one of a pair, 56in. high. £800

A leaded and stained glass panel by George Walton, after a design by Charles Rennie Mackintosh, 133.6cm. high, 91.4cm. wide. £660

An Art Nouveau rectangular leaded glass panel, by Jacques Gruber, 256cm. high. £9,720

A 15th century, perhaps English, leaded glass niche-shaped window, 17¼ x 5¼in. £600

A set of four late 18th or early 19th century English painted glass panels of female allegories of Justice, Faith, Hope and Charity, probably by Thos. Jarvis, after Sir J. Reynolds, each panel 72 x 40cm. £2,090

One of a pair of Gruber leaded glass doors, 1920's, 180cm. wide. £2,200

GLASS

STANGENGLAS

Late 16th century enamelled armorial 'Stangenglas', S. German or Hall, 27.5cm. high. £1,320

A German enamelled 'Stangenglas' for Augustus Sudoflen, Saxony or Bohemia, 1658, 23cm. high. £2,750

Late 16th century enamelled armorial 'Stangenglas', S. German or Hall, 26cm. high. £1,320

SWEETMEAT GLASSES

Mid 18th century moulded pedestal stemmed sweetmeat glass, 16.5cm. high. £418

A sweetmeat glass, the shallow flared bucket bowl with gadrooned underside and folded rim, circa 1730, 9.5cm. high. £367

A sweetmeat glass supported on a scallop-edged foot, 6¼in. high, circa 1770. £60

A 16th/17th century Facon de Venise sweetmeat dish with ribbed bowl, 11.5cm. high. £990

One of a set of six late 19th century sweetmeat glasses in neo-baroque style, 11cm. high. £1,760

Bohemian armorial sweetmeat glass with boat-shaped bowl, 11cm. high, circa 1720-30. £500

GLASS

SYRUP DISPENSERS

'Cherry Chic' syrup dispenser, manufactured by J. Hungerford Smith, New York, circa 1925, 11½in. high. £1,125

'Hires' syrup dispenser, Phila., patented 1920, 14¼in. high. £265

'Orange-Julep' syrup dispenser, circa 1920, 14¼in. high. £390

SYPHONS

Greenock Apothecaries & Lawsons Ltd. soda syphon, circa 1902. £6

Table syphon by J. Burgess, 12in. tall. £6

T. Mason & Sons, Manufacturers of High Class Table Waters, Smethwick, fluted blue glass syphon. £8

An early Sparklets wire-bound soda syphon. £10

Blue glass soda syphon inscribed Job Wragg Ltd., with acid etching on front, dated 1902. £12

Spaco Ltd. Royal Leamington Spa blue glass soda syphon with silver plated top. £12

SYPHONS

Art Deco style plated
Sparklets type syphon,
29cm. high.   £10

A clear glass Schweppes
sample syphon, 16cm.
high.   £20

Amber glass writhened
syphon by Parker Bros.
of Drighlington, 31cm.
high.   £25

One shot, basket
covered, Sparklets type
syphon, 32cm. high.
                          £8

Pink faceted glass
syphon by Maps,
illustrated with a figure
of a man, 33cm. high.
                          £18

Basket covered Gaza-
teur syphon with a
porcelain base, 45cm.
high.   £50

Yellow glass syphon by
L. G. Weeks & Sons of
Torrington, 33cm.
high.   £16

Seltzogene twin bulbed
syphon made by D.
Fevre, Paris, 45cm.
high.   £30

SYPHONS

Early cobalt blue syphon by S. J. Coley of Stroud with patented porcelain top, 30cm. high.   £25

Faceted clear glass syphon by Wrights of Walkery, 31cm. high.   £16

Miniature blue/green glass syphon by the Dorset Mineral Water Co. of Poole, 17½cm. high.   £30

Sparklet clear glass, mesh covered syphon, circa 1925, 37cm. high.   £10

Green glass syphon by the Victoria Wine Co. illustrated with a picture of Queen Victoria, 33cm. high.   £16

Sparklet syphon charger used by hotels to refill syphons, 39cm. high.   £35

Loze's patent Seltzogene mesh covered syphon, circa 1900, 45cm. high.   £50

Job Wragg of Birmingham clear glass syphon illustrated with a picture of the syphon in use in red print, 31cm. high.   £10

GLASS

Bohemian Hausmalerei opaque-opaline glass tankard and cover of barrel shape, circa 1750, 16.5cm. high.   £1,000

Mid 18th century Russian Imperial tankard with pewter thumbpiece and cover, 22.5cm. high.   £750

Tiffany gold iridescent loving cup with three handles, 5in. high.   £500

One of a pair of Liberty Tudric mugs designed by A. Knox with original green glass liners by J. Powell & Son, circa 1900, 13cm. high.   £130

Early 18th century opaque glass mug of stoneware form, 9.2cm. £462

Late 18th century Bohemian engraved tankard and cover with faceted finial, 20cm. high.   £1,250

Central Germany Farrier's Guild dated cylindrical tankard, 1762, 18.5cm. high.   £2,500

Mid 18th century Central European cylindrical tankard with pewter cover, 21.5cm. high.   £750

Saxon dated cylindrical tankard with engraved body, dated 1763, 13.5cm. high.   £750

TANKARDS & MUGS

A Bohemian 'Tiefschnitt' tankard and silver-mounted porcelain cover, attributed to F. Zach, circa 1855-60, 16cm. high.
£455

18th century Central European tankard with hinged pewter cover, 15cm. high.   £1,000

An 18th century enamelled milchglas tankard of barrel form, 18cm. high.
£250

A Bohemian enamelled and gilt tankard and cover in opaque-pink glass with applied scroll handle, 20cm. high, circa 1840-60.
£660

An engraved tankard of cylindrical form, circa 1830, 11cm. high.
£350

16th century South Netherlands Facon de Venise tankard with hinged pewter cover, 16.5cm. high.   £4,000

A pink-stained engraved spa tankard and cover, circa 1850, 18.2cm.
£660

Mid 18th century Central European milchglas tankard, 10.3cm. high.
£450

A Victorian silver mounted glass tankard by Elkington & Co., Birmingham, 1859, 9in. high.
£1,750

TANTALUS

An Edwardian inlaid
mahogany tantalus with
three cut glass whisky
decanters and stoppers.
£260

An engraved silver-plated
tantalus on ball feet containing three square cut
glass decanters.   £400

An oak cased three-bottle
tantalus with cigar drawer.
£200

Mid 19th century scarlet boulle
tantalus with fitted interior,
13½in. wide.   £600

A Victorian two bottle
tantalus with silver plated
mounts, 13¼in. long
overall.   £290

Mid 19th century Black
Forest tantalus of table
cabinet form, 19in. high.
£325

Victorian silver plated two-
bottle tantalus, circa 1875,
12½in. high.   £500

An oak tantalus containing
three square cut glass decanters with prismatic stoppers.
£200

Victorian coromandel wood
and brass tantalus with three
bottles, 12in. wide.   £400

TAZZAS

Mid 17th century Facon-
de-Venise filigree tazza,
31cm. diam. £734

16th century Nether-
lands Facon de Venise
'ice glass' tazza with
shallow tray, 15.8cm.
diam. £4,000

A 17th century Venetian
diamond engraved tazza,
20cm. diam. £1,980

A 16th/17th century
Facon de Venise tazza
with ribbed saucer-
shaped bowl, 14.5cm.
£1,210

Late 16th century Spanish
Facon de Venise diamond-
engraved tazza with octa-
foil tray, 16.5cm. high.
£6,500

Mid 16th century Facon
de Venise tazza with
shallow tray, perhaps
Antwerp, 18cm. diam.
£5,000

TEAPOTS

A Schott & Gen Jena
glass teapot, 1930-34.
£550

A Schott & Gen 'Jena er Glas' clear glass
teaset, designed by Wm. Wagenfeld, teapot, cover and filter, 11cm. high. £350

Mid 18th century Russian
engraved glass teapot with
applied spout and handle,
14.5cm.high. £2,500

A Bohemian 'Zwischengoldglas' flared tumbler, circa 1730, 9cm. high. £660

Bohemian 'Zwischengold' tumbler with double-walled body, circa 1730, 6cm. high. £1,300

Beilby tumbler, flared sides enamelled in white, 10cm. high, circa 1765. £1,000

An Austrian 'Zwischengold' Armorial tumbler by Johann Mildner, set with a double walled medallion, circa 1794, 12cm. high. £3,200

A Viennese transparent enamelled topographical tumbler, attributed to G. Samuel Mohn, 1815-20, 9cm. high. £2,420

Possibly late 18th century Central European enamelled 'Jagd' tumbler, 16.5cm. high. £3,740

A Baccarat moulded enamelled cylindrical tumbler, decorated in colours on gilt foil, 9cm. high. £259

A Charpentier dated cylindrical tumbler engraved with Cupid standing beside an urn, circa 1823, 9cm. high. £500

A Bohemian 'Zwischengoldglas' fluted tumbler, initialled 'IHS', circa 1730, 8cm. high. £850

GLASS

Bohemian 'Zwischengold' tumbler with faceted body, circa 1730, 6cm. high. £750

Bohemian engraved tumbler, with flared faceted sides, circa 1720-30, 8.7cm. high. £750

A plated amberina tumbler, New Bedford Glass Co., Mass., circa 1886, 3¾in. high. £555

A Bohemian pale blue hexagonal waisted tumbler decorated in silver, circa 1835, 12cm. high. £455

A Baccarat double medal cylindrical tumbler with cut foot and sunray base, 10.5cm. high. £770

A Bohemian cut glass coin tumbler, circa 1830, 12.5cm. high. £374

Late 18th/early 19th century engraved Masonic toasting glass, 4¾in. high. £993

A Continental blue pressed glass, Royal portrait tumbler, perhaps Bercy, Paris, circa 1840, 11cm. high. £270

A peachblow agate tumbler, New England Glass Co., Mass., circa 1887, 3.5/8in. high. £332

197

TUMBLERS

A 19th century sulphide and crystal Baccarat tumbler, 'General Lafayette', 4in. high.　£735

Bohemian marbled tumbler with flared faceted sides, 5.7cm. high, circa 1730.
　　　　　　　£2,750

One of a pair of 'Lynn' flared tumblers with horizontally ribbed sides, circa 1775, 11.5cm. high.　£176

A Bohemian octagonal flared tumbler with waisted foot, circa 1845, 13cm. high.　£345

A lower Austrian 'Zwischengold' tumbler by Johann Mildner, the cylindrical body set with a double-walled medallion, circa 1788, 8.5cm. high.　£850

A N. Bohemian transparent enamelled armorial tumbler, circa 1835, 12cm. high.
　　　　　　　£1,320

A plated amberina tumbler, New Bedford Glass Co., Mass., circa 1886, 3¾in. high.　£699

A Charpentier engraved cylindrical tumbler with a recumbent sheep, a dog, hat and crook, circa 1820, 9cm. high.　£420

A gilt decorated blue tumbler from the atelier of James Giles, circa 1765, 10.5cm. high.　£748

TUMBLERS

A Bohemian engraved cylindrical tumbler, circa 1825,
10cm. high.   £528

'Mountain Dew' Scotch
whisky glass by Robertson,
Sanderson & Co., Leith.
£15

Late 18th century flared
tumbler, 9cm. high.£75

A Bohemian pale green flared
octagonal tumbler on spreading foot, mid 19th century,
12cm. high.   £370

A Baccarat enamelled cut
glass tumbler, the plaque
decorated in coloured enamels on gilt foil, 8.5cm.
high.   £540

A Bohemian cobalt blue
octagonal tumbler with
waved foot, circa 1845,
13cm. high.   £345

One of a pair of cut glass
tumblers with sterling
silver mountings, Russia,
circa 1900, 4in. high.
£255

Green opaque art glass
tumbler, New England Glass
Co., Mass., 1887, 3.7/8in.
high.   £314

A Bohemian ruby overlay
engraved tumbler of flared
form, circa 1860, 12.5cm.
high.   £432

VASES

A Louis XVI ormolu mounted blue glass vase and cover, 11in. high.   £275

Mid 19th century pearl satin-glass ovoid vase with frilled auricular lip, 15.2cm.   £290

A Venetian green glass bud vase, designed as a dolphin on circular foot, circa 1920, 7in. high.   £20

An ormolu mounted cut glass vase of slightly tapering form with waved top and ram mask handles, 14in. high.   £330

A Verlys pale amber-coloured moulded glass vase with everted rim, France, circa 1930, 22.5cm. high.   £100

A Le Verre Francais overlay and acid etched vase, the white and amber mottled glass decorated with amethyst stylized tulips, 39.5cm. high.   £220

A Verlys moulded glass vase, France, circa 1930, 28.5cm. high.   £200

A Schneider vase, the mottled orange, yellow and blue glass blown through a wrought-iron mount, 29.3cm. high.   £280

A Fratelli Toso two-handled 'murrina' vase in cobalt blue, white and green, circa 1910, 32.5cm. high.   £755

VASES

A Nuutajarvi Notsjo vase, designed by Gunnel Nyman, 38.8cm. high. £352

Libbey cut glass flower centre with sawtoothed rim, Ohio, circa 1910, 9½in. diam. £570

An Italian blown glass vase by Luciano Ferro, 40.5cm., 1950's. £1,100

Mother-of-pearl art glass vase in Federzeichnung design, circa 1900, patent 9159, (English control marks), 11½in. high. £664

A James Powell vase, milky vaseline glass, the flattened bulbous base pinched into four arms supporting a floppy quatrefoil rim, 16.5cm. high. £440

A tall Le Verre Francais overlay acid etched vase, the milky-white and yellow mottled glass overlaid with mottled green, brown and orange glass, 48cm. high. £440

An Aureliano Toso vase of asymmetric double-gourd shape, clear glass with thin white latticinio stripes, 27.4cm. high. £1,540

Quezal floriform vase with ruffled rim and gold interior, New York, circa 1910, 5.3/8in. high. £490

Victorian brown cameo over opal vase, by George Woodall, circa 1895, 8in. high. £2,050

An Almeric Walter pate-
de-verre vase of amber
yellow glass, modelled
by Henri Berge, 6½in.
high. £750

A Kosta vase, designed by
Vicke Lindstrand, bottle-
shaped, circa 1955, 32.5cm.
high. £440

A clear glass hexagonal
vase designed by Elis
Bergh for Kosta. £80

Mid 19th century decalcomania
slender oviform vase and a
ball cover, the vase 40.5cm.
high. £880

A Kosta cameo glass vase
designed by Gunnar
Wenneberg, circa 1900,
17cm. high. £320

Three Vistosi tall bottle vases,
designed by Peter Pelzel, circa
1960, 43.5cm., 41cm. and 34cm.
£1,320

A Cenedese vase, milky glass
partly overlaid with white,
the decoration and rim in
deep amethyst-coloured
glass, 34cm. high. £825

Crystal glass two-handled vase,
on four short feet, engraved with
a portrait of Baden Powell, 11in.
high. £12

A Richard cameo glass vase
overlaid in brown and red,
13½in. high. £400

VASES

A 19th century pink glass spill vase of elongated trumpet form, 12½in. high. £30

A large Legras cameo glass landscape vase, circa 1900, 29.5cm. high. £770

A large Sabino opalescent glass vase, 1930. £330

A glass vase and cover attributed to Fachschule Haida, circa 1910, 32cm. high. £216

A large Regency ormolu and cut glass vase, the urn-shaped body set with faceted cabochons in latticework frame, 22in. high. £11,340

A Le Verre Francais overlay acid etched vase, the pinkish-white mottled glass overlaid with amethyst stylised chrysanthemums, 32cm. high. £550

A tall Legras acid etched vase, the milky-white and blue glass with trapped air inclusions, 41cm. high. £440

A Sabino blue opalescent glass elongated vase, 29.2cm. high. £275

Early 20th century Quezal Art Glass vase, New York, signed, 8¼in. high. £490

VASES

Mid 19th century engraved opaque white glass vase, 24in. high.   £820

One of a pair of amethyst celery vases, Mass., circa 1850, 10in. high.   £690

A Vallerysthal enamelled and acid etched vase, 24.9cm. high.   £440

An iridescent tear vase, attributed to Meyr's Neffe, the pinkish-green glass with silvery blue streak decoration, 22.3cm. high.   £864

A 19th century Viennese rock crystal and enamel vase in the form of a fish, the cover surmounted by an enamelled figure of Neptune, 31cm. high.   £9,000

One of a pair of pink-flash narrow tapering two-handled vases, 16½in. high.   £700

One of a pair of late 18th century ormolu and blue cut glass vases, Swedish or Russian, 9½in. high.   £3,080

A pair of Lithyalin vases, in sealing wax red glass, with trumpet necks and circular feet, 23cm. high. |£650

One of a pair of Moser vases, the clear and amethyst tinted glass carved and engraved with flowers, 26.5cm. high.   £330

A free-form internally decorated glass vase, designed and made by Aldo Nasson, 1950's 23cm.
£770

A 19th century Pekin glass vase with six fan-shaped feet, 8¼in. high.
£506

A small cylindrical over-laid iridescent glass vase, circa 1900, 11.5cm. high.
£200

An Aldo Nasson double-neck organic-form glass vase, inscribed Nasson, 14½in. high.
£200

A free-hand ware vase by the Imperial Glass Co., Ohio, 1920's, 5.7/8in. high.
£205

A clear glass vase, the cylindrical shape pulled out on one side to form two oval prunts, engraved Vistosi 1970, 28.5cm. high.
£715

A vase with shouldered tapering body and flared neck, circa 1850, 17.4cm. high.
£145

A Ferdinand Poschinger Glass-huten vase, the pale green glass with combed deep red 'peacock feather' design, 25cm. high.
£1,080

A blue-flashed and acid-etched cylindrical vase of the Art Deco period.
£100

VASES

A large Fulvio Bianconi vase of flattened flaring cylindrical shape, 1957, 39cm. high.   £1,620

A James Powell vase, milky vaseline glass, the body narrowing at the shoulder to a frilled rim, 30cm. high.   £385

Victorian red overlay glass vase, 1860.   £44

A Val Saint Lambert elongated baluster enamelled and acid etched vase, 40.1cm. high.   £2,310

An Almeric Walter pate-de-verre two-handled mortar pattern vase, designed by Henri Berge, 5in. high.   £1,050

An Italian 17th century ormolu mounted amethyst-tinted vase, 34.5cm. high.   £990

A Ver Centre vase, elongated ovoid shape enamel painted in various colours over a green ground, signature Ver Centre 1927, 29cm. high.   £1,080

One of a pair of WMF pewter and glass vases, stamped marks, 48cm. high.   £550

An Arsale overlay glass vase, the flattened slender pear shaped body overlaid with russet-coloured glass, 31.6cm. high.   £302

VASES

Art Nouveau gourd-
shaped vase, iridescent
and silver overlaid, signed
W.H. Saxton, 8in. high.
£525

Early 20th century cut glass
flower centre, America,
9.1/8in. high. £559

A 19th century French
green glass vase, the tulip-
shaped bowl with crenellated
rim, 36cm. high. £100

An 18th century Spanish
four-handled vase of transparent greenish tint, 22cm.
high. £100

A campana shaped vase, star
and stud cut with faceted
knop to stem, 10½in. high.
£40

A French glass vase of elliptical
section, 24.5cm. high, stamped
with poincon and maker's mark
JM in lozenge. £380

A patchwork glass vase,
by Dino Martens, 26cm.,
1950's. £880

A Wiener Werkstatte amethyst
glass vase and cover designed
by Josef Hoffmann, 17cm.
high. £702

A vase attributed to Ferro
Lazzarini and the design
to Flavio Poli, circa 1960,
32cm. high. £990

VASES
ARGY-ROUSSEAU

A G. Argy-Rousseau pate-de-verre vase, numbered 16485, 26.5cm. high. £5,280

A Gabriel Argy-Rousseau pate-de-verre vase, 12cm. high. £2,090

French Art Nouveau pate de verre vase, signed G. Argy-Rousseau, circa 1900, 3.7/8in. high. £650

An Argy-Rousseau pate-de-verre vase, France, circa 1925, 15.2cm. high. £2,700

A Gabriel Argy-Rousseau pate-de-verre vase, the body moulded with black spiders spinning their webs amongst leaves, 4¾in. high. £3,520

A Gabriel Argy-Rousseau pate-de-verre vase, the body moulded with tall stemmed plants with hanging red pods, 6in. high. £1,980

A Gabriel Argy-Rousseau tall pate-de-verre vase, 26cm. high. £4,950

A Gabriel Argy-Rousseau pate-de-verre vase of swollen cylindrical shape, 9.5cm. high. £1,540

A pate-de-verre oviform vase by Gabriel Argy-Rousseau, 24cm. high. £1,620

VASES
BAROVIER

A large Barovier & Toso patchwork vase, the white and mauve glass forming a checker-pattern overall, 44.5cm. high. £2,200

A patchwork vase attributed to Barovier, large ovoid shape, with a herring-bone patchwork design in amethyst, milky and clear glass, 24.5cm. high. £540

A vase attributed to Barovier, of flattened urn shape, 29.1cm. high. £1,026

BEIJING

A Qianlong Beijing translucent red glass, pear-shaped vase, 11.5cm. high. £518

A Beijing semi-translucent rose glass slender oviform vase, 19.5cm. high. £3,564

A Beijing glass double gourd vase of mustard-yellow tone, 9in. high. £660

BOHEMIAN

A Bohemian ruby flashed vase and cover, on faceted knopped stem and lobed foot, 58cm. high. £3,200

A pair of Bohemian ruby glass vases of slender ovoid pedestal form, 45.5cm. high. £980

A Bohemian vase flashed in ruby and engraved with stags in woodland, 46cm. high. £1,100

VASES
CAMEO GLASS

A blue and white cameo glass vase with tapering ovoid body, 1880's, 21cm. high. £990

A cameo glass vase of shouldered ovoid form in rich blue and opaque white, 1880's, 14.7cm. £715

A carved cameo glass vase, 1890's. £1,760

A Russian cameo glass vase, the milky-white martele glass overlaid with amber stylised leaves, 17cm. high. £825

A yellow ground cameo vase of compressed form, circa 1890, 22cm. high. £918

A ruby and white cameo glass vase of shouldered ovoid form, 1880's, 22cm. £1,250

D' ARGENTAL

A cameo glass cone-shaped vase by D'Argental, 12.3cm. high. £280

D'Argental French cameo cut vase, circa 1890, 13in. diam. £600

A D'Argental cameo bowl with trefoil rim, overlaid in claret-coloured glass with water-lily and lily-pad on a pond against a pale amber ground, 16cm. diam. £660

VASES
DAUM

Late 19th century Daum Nancy acid finished bud vase, France, 4½in. high. **£190**

A large Daum green tinted etched glass vase, 32cm., 1930's. **£286**

A Daum acid etched and enamelled landscape slender baluster vase, 50.1cm. high. **£1,512**

A Daum double overlay cameo glass and acid-etched vase, engraved with cross of Lorraine, 50.3cm. high. **£2,160**

A Daum Art Deco acid etched vase, bell-shaped, 28cm. high. **£605**

A Daum internally decorated engraved and applied glass vase of slender shouldered form and bulbous flaring neck, 35cm. high. **£55,000**

A Daum cameo glass tall slender baluster vase with waisted base, circa 1900, 52cm. high. **£1,400**

A Daum vase with barrel-shaped body with four lug handles, circa 1930, 26.5cm. high. **£885**

A Daum vase, circular base and waisted cylindrical shape with flared rim, 35.1cm. high. **£715**

VASES
DAUM

A Daum etched glass vase, circa 1930. £110

One of a pair of green Art glass cylindrical vases, signed Daum, Nancy, 11in. high. £200

A green Art glass conical-shaped vase, signed Daum Nancy, 8½in. wide. £70

A Daum glass spill vase etched with a mistletoe sprig, circa 1900. £220

A Daum carved and acid etched vase, inscribed with Cross of Lorraine, 23.8cm. high. £3,240

A Daum cameo vase of tall cylindrical shape with slightly everted rim and compressed globular base, 29.1cm. high. £2,916

A Daum enamelled and acid etched vase of rounded cube form, enamelled in white, black and grey, with blackbirds in winter landscape, 15.2cm. diam. £1,760

A Daum glass vase, 39.3cm. high, signed 'Daum Nancy' in gilt on base. £2,500

A Daum enamelled and acid etched vase of rounded cube form, 11.5cm. high. £1,430

VASES
DAUM

A Daum double-overlay carved vase of flattened globular shape, 11.5cm. high.   £715

A green Art glass three-tier-shaped vase, signed Daum Nancy, 13in. high.   £75

Daum semi-cameo shaped rectangular vase, signed, 4¼in. high.   £360

A tall Daum cameo vase with bulbous neck, with Cross of Lorraine, 50.2cm. high.   £1,080

A small Daum carved and acid etched vase of boat shape, engraved signature Daum Nancy with the Cross of Lorraine, 10.5cm. high.   £2,640

A Daum cameo vase, the matt yellow, amethyst and green ground overlaid in shaded claret-coloured glass, 26.3cm. high.   £3,024

A Daum Art Deco acid etched vase, oviform with tall neck, 29cm. high.   £935

A tall Daum carved and acid etched mould-blown vase, baluster shape, engraved with the Cross of Lorraine, 44cm. high.   £2,640

A Daum cameo and engraved martele flattened globular glass vase, 13.8cm. high.   £1,620

VASES
DAUM

A Daum vase with cameo-cut and enamel painted winter landscape on acid treated matt pale amber ground, 25cm. high.   £1,045

A miniature Daum enamelled and acid etched vase enamelled with Sweet Violets, 4.3cm. high.   £484

A Daum enamelled and acid etched vase, enamelled Daum Nancy with Cross of Lorraine, 21.6cm. high.   £770

A Daum cameo and engraved martele vase, the hammered green, orange and clear ground overlaid with iris flower, 16.7cm. high.   £1,080

A Daum acid textured two-handled vase, engraved signature Daum Nancy with the Cross of Lorraine, France, 25.5cm. high.   £880

A Daum cameo vase, overlaid in mottled russet red, orange, green and black, carved with brambles, 61.1cm. high.   £1,728

A Daum cameo and engraved martele baluster vase, engraved Daum Nancy with Cross of Lorraine, 25.4cm. high.   £1,870

A Daum Art Deco acid etched vase, the smoky-blue glass deeply etched with oval and circular panels, 33.5cm. high.   £1,430

A Daum cameo landscape vase, the tapering cylindrical body with swollen collar, 27cm. high.   £540

VASES
DELATTE

A Delatte cameo glass land-scape vase, broad baluster shape with cylindrical neck, 33.1cm. high. £540

A tall Delatte cameo vase, overlaid in deep amber-coloured glass with sprays of marsh orchid, 50cm. high. £432

A Delatte enamelled glass vase, slender ovoid with flared rim and pad foot, 1920's, 21.25cm. high. £130

ELTON

An Elton baluster vase, the neck with six loop handles, 19cm. high. £170

An Elton globular vase with tall neck and flared rim, over-all crackled gold lustre glaze, 19cm. high. £230

An Elton single-handled vase of waisted baluster form, overall gold lustre crackle glaze, 22cm. high. £250

FACON DE VENISE

Late 16th century Vene-tian Facon de Venise filigree two-handled vase, 24cm. high. £600

Late 17th/early 18th century Facon-de-Venise filigree vase, 20.5cm. high. £572

A Facon de Venise fili-gree vase of miniature 'albarello' form, circa 1600, 8.5cm. high. £374

VASES
GALLE

A double overlay slender
pear-shaped landscape
vase by Emile Galle,
49.5cm. high.   £648

Galle cameo glass vase
with short everted neck,
circa 1900, 11.5cm. high.
£650

An applied overlay, intercalaire, fire-polished and
verre parlant glass vase
by Emile Galle, 22cm.
high.   £1,728

A carved double-overlay
cameo vase, bearing an
incised Galle chinoiserie
signature, 25cm. high.
£2,200

A Galle blowout vase with
flowering clematis in shaded
purple on a yellow ground,
25.5cm. high.   £3,456

A Galle cameo glass vase, the
flattened spherical body with
slender stem overlaid in red
and etched with berried foliage, 7in. high.   £462

A Galle cameo vase with
carved and acid etched decoration of a lakeside scene,
the yellow glass overlaid
with brown, 26.5cm. high.
£1,620

A Galle carved acid etched
triple overlay landscape
vase, 50.5cm. high. £6,600

A Galle double overlay
martele carved and acid
etched vase of goblet shape,
15.5cm. high.   £8,800

VASES
GALLE

A Galle cameo glass vase
of slender ovoid form,
9¼in. high.   £450

A parcel gilt mounted,
wheel carved, overlay
and intercalaire glass
vase by Emile Galle,
13cm. high.   £3,024

Galle cameo glass vase,
etched with flowers and
butterflies, 1904, 32.5cm.
high.   £650

A Galle double overlay
carved and acid etched vase,
the light green glass overlaid
with ferns in shades of green
and light brown, 41cm. high.
                        £1,650

Late 19th century Galle
cameo glass vase, signed,
France, 8¼in. high. £300

A Galle cameo baluster
vase, the amber and milky
white glass overlaid in
purple, carved with fuschia,
16cm. high.   £550

A Galle double overlay
carved and acid etched landscape vase, the yellow glass
overlaid with amethyst trees,
32cm. high.   £2,750

A Galle fire-polished cameo vase,
purple glass cut back to a ground
shading from purple to milky-
white coloured glass, 18.5cm.
high.   £2,592

A Galle carved and acid-
etched vase, the amber glass
overlaid with green oak leaves
and acorns, 40cm. high. £990

VASES
GALLE

Late 19th century Galle
cameo glass vase with
inverted rim, signed,
11¾in. high.   £650

An enamelled and acid
etched rectangular jar
by Emile Galle, 14.2cm.
high.   £300

A Galle cameo glass land-
scape vase, circa 1900,
59cm. high.   £2,420

A Galle etched and double
overlay glass vase, the aqua-
marine glass overlaid in
white and brown and etched
with penguins, 20.3cm. high.
                £12,100

A Galle cameo glass moon-
shaped vase, 7in. high.
                £1,000

'Roses de France', a Galle
internally decorated, applied
martele and overlay glass
vase of pear shape, 19.2cm.
high.   £52,800

A Galle cameo glass and fire-
polished shaped cylindrical
vase, circa 1900, 19.9cm.
high.   £560

A Galle triple cameo fire-
polished vase, waisted and
flaring cylindrical shape,
49.1cm. high.   £2,160

A Galle moulded blown and
cameo glass vase of tapering
baluster form on circular
foot, circa 1900, 29.2cm.
high.   £5,940

VASES
GALLE

Small Galle cameo glass
vase with squat trumpet
body, signed, circa 1900,
10.5cm. high.   £400

A double overlay slender
oviform vase by Emile
Galle, 37cm. high. £1,728

A very important Galle
glass vase, signed,
20.5cm. high, circa
1900.   £47,435

A large Galle carved and
acid etched double-
overlay 'vase aux ombelles',
with cameo signature Galle,
63.5cm. high.   £3,300

A Galle double overlay carved
blow out vase, the amber glass
overlaid with fruiting vines,
27.5cm. high.   £4,950

A Galle cameo glass vase of
flared cylindrical shape,
31.5cm. high, signed with
sinuous cameo 'Galle'.
                    £2,800

A large Galle cameo glass
vase, pale amber over a
ground shading from blue
to yellow, circa 1900,
48.6cm. high.   £4,320

One of a pair of Galle fire-
polished urn-shaped vases,
one vase inscribed with
Galle depose, 26.9cm. high.
                    £2,052

An artistic Galle 'verrerie
parlante' vase, engraved
Galle expos 1900, 41.5cm.
high.   £52,800

VASES
GALLE

A Galle cameo glass
vase in yellow glass tin-
ted pink at the neck,
circa 1900, 29.5cm.
high. £700

A Galle agate glass vase
with intaglio decoration,
circa 1900, 15cm. diam.
£1,760

Galle cameo glass vase
in grey glass overlaid in
purple, circa 1900,
signed, 19cm. high.
£575

A small Galle cameo
glass 'blow out' vase,
circa 1900, 18.5cm.
high. £900

A Galle carved and fire-
polished vase, the glass shading from purple to milky
white and amber with silver
foil inclusions, 32.5cm. high.
£6,600

A Galle cameo vase, the
flattened globular body on
splayed foot, 23.5cm. high.
£1,188

A large Galle cameo glass
vase, blue glass over a frosted base with stylised floral
and foliate decoration, circa
1900, 72.2cm. high. £1,728

A Galle cameo glass vase,
overlaid in deep mauve
with sprays of laburnum,
circa 1900, 31.3cm. high.
£682

A Galle acid etched and
enamelled soli-fleur glass
vase, the cylindrical body
with ribbed and splayed
base, 31.6cm. high. £972

VASES
GALLE

A Galle cameo glass vase
of tapered form and cir-
cular section, circa 1900,
45.5cm. high.   £1,850

Galle cameo glass vase
of teardrop form, circa
1900, 15.5cm. high.
£450

A Galle acid etched and
enamelled soli-fleur vase,
inscribed Cristallerie d'Emile
Galle Nancy, 49.4cm. high.
£1,296

A tall Galle double overlay
landscape vase, the matt pale
white ground overlaid in
brown, green and amber
polished glass with daffodils,
41.8cm. high.   £1,620

A spherical cameo glass
vase with everted rim by
Emile Galle, 22.9cm.
high.   £2,500

A Galle fire polished cameo
glass vase of squat oviform
with flaring stem, 17in.
high, inscribed.   £650

An ovoid Galle cameo
glass vase in green glass
streaked with inky blue,
circa 1900, 12.5cm.
high.   £1,500

A Galle marqueterie de verre
vase, bun foot with body
shaped like a crocus bloom,
circa 1900, 35cm. high.
£9,180

A Galle cameo glass 'blow
out' vase, circa 1900,
32.5cm. high.   £4,000

VASES
GALLE

Small Galle cameo glass vase with squat flared base, circa 1900, 10.25cm. £350

Galle cameo glass vase with flared trumpet body, signed, circa 1900 24.5cm. high. £500

A Galle carved acid etched and fire-polished vase, 23.5cm. high. £1,980

A Galle internally decorated vase, the amber-coloured glass decorated with dark red streaks, engraved Cristallerie de Galle, 20cm. high. £2,200

A Galle vase, pale amber-coloured glass with gold foil inclusions overlaid with white and blue, 18.5cm. high. £2,200

A Galle cameo vase, the matt amber ground overlaid in shaded claret-coloured glass, 45.5cm. high. £3,520

A Galle acid etched and enamelled vase with cylindrical body and spreading base, 34.9cm. high. £648

A Galle double overlay carved vase, the shaded grey and green glass overlaid with dark amethyst and violet bindweeds, 13.5cm. high. £550

A Galle carved and acid etched double-overlay landscape vase, 29cm. high. £5,280

VASES
GALLE

A Galle cameo glass vase, the oviform body with flaring neck, 5¼in. high. £242

A Galle double overlay cameo oviform vase with cylindrical neck, overlaid in lilac and green, 18.4cm. high. £540

A Galle marqueterie-sur-verre vase of cylindrical shape, engraved Galle etude, circa 1895, 19.5cm. high. £11,000

A tall Galle double overlay landscape baluster vase with everted rim and circular base, 45.9cm. high. £4,620

A massive Galle triple cameo vase with acid etched and carved decoration of lilies, 85.5cm. high. £7,020

A Galle cameo vase overlaid with brown glass etched with orchid spray against a mottled green, blue and opaque ground, 18.5cm. high. £432

One of a pair of small Galle enamelled glass vases with bulbous base, 5½in. high. £200

A Galle double overlay carved and acid-etched vase, the milky-white glass decorated with dark brown pine trees, 15cm. high. £660

A Galle double overlay carved and acid etched vase, the shaded green, white and pink glass overlaid with brown and green trees, 47cm. high. £2,860

VASES
LALIQUE

'Marise', a Lalique opalescent glass vase, the body moulded with shoals of fish, 9½in. high.   £1,350

'Beliers', a Lalique vase with two handles moulded as rams, 19cm. high. £550

Rene Lalique opalescent glass vase with flared rim, 12in. diam. £3,666

'Six Figurines et Masques', a Lalique opalescent vase moulded with nude females, 25cm. high.   £2,200

'Albert', a Lalique vase, the topaz glass with two handles moulded as eagles' heads, 17.3cm. high.   £1,045

A Lalique cylindrical glass vase, 'Coqs et Plumes', circa 1930, 15.4cm. high.   £345

A Lalique clear and frosted glass vase, 'Aigrettes', inscribed, 10in. high.   £850

'Violettes', a Lalique vase, the satin finished opalescent glass partially blue stained and moulded with eight overlapping leaves, 15.7cm. high.   £880

'Alicante', a Lalique blue opalescent vase, satin finished glass moulded with a band of six parakeet heads among wheatears, 25.7cm. high.   £3,740

VASES
LALIQUE

A Lalique vase, 'Yvelines', grey tinted clear and satin finished glass moulded with lug handles, circa 1930, 20cm. high. £453

'Languedoc', a Lalique vase, the body deeply moulded with bands of stylised leaves, 22.6cm. high. £1,320

Rene Lalique opalescent glass vase with thistle pattern, 9in. high. £1,000

'Camargue', a Lalique frosted glass vase, moulded with horses in amber stained cartouches, 28.5cm. high. £3,190

'Gui', a Lalique vase, the clear satin finished glass with turquoise staining moulded with branches of mistletoe, 17.2cm. high. £250

A Lalique opalescent glass vase with moulded nodule decoration, 7in. high. £200

'Perruches', a blue Lalique oviform vase, 25.9cm. high. £3,240

A Lalique blue opalescent vase, Ceylan, the satin-finished glass moulded with band of budgerigars, 24.2cm. high. £1,210

'Formose', a Lalique opalescent vase, moulded with a shoal of goldfish, 17cm. high. £432

VASES
LALIQUE

A Lalique blue stained glass vase, globular with everted neck, 7¼in. high. £320

'Caudebec', a Lalique vase with two semi-circular handles, 14.5cm. high. £550

A Lalique opalescent glass vase of ovoid shape, 1930's, 18cm. high. £154

'Rampillon', an opalescent Lalique vase, 12.6cm. high. £374

A green Lalique vase, Epicea, with moulded overall decoration of palm fronds, 23.5cm. high. £2,420

Lalique smokey-grey flared vase, cobweb design in relief, 9½in. high. £1,100

'Formose', a green Lalique vase, the clear and satin glass moulded with goldfish, 17cm. high. £1,188

A Lalique baluster vase, the clear satin finished glass moulded with bands of roses with blue staining, 23.6cm. high. £462

A Lalique globular vase, 'Gui', the opalescent glass moulded with intertwined fruiting mistletoe, circa 1930, 16.9cm. high. £345

VASES
LALIQUE

A Lalique opalescent
glass vase 'Poissons',
8¾in. high.   £500

A Lalique compressed
globular frosted glass vase,
'Languedoc', 8¾in. high.
£900

'Palissy', a Lalique green tinted
vase, the satin finished glass
moulded with snail shells,
15.8cm. high.   £176

A Lalique vase, the milky
opaque glass moulded with
intertwined brambles,
23cm. high.   £484

'Fountainebleu', a Lalique
blue glass vase, the body
moulded with fruit-laden
trailing vines, 17.4cm. high.
£972

Lalique pale brown opaque
glass, 'Six Figurines et
Masques' vase, 9½in. high.
£1,400

'Chamois', an amber Lalique
vase, the green stained clear and
satin finished glass moulded
with stylised antelopes, 12cm.
high.   £770

A Lalique opalescent glass
vase, 'Bacchantes', 9½in.
high.   £2,800

'Formose', a Lalique opalescent globular vase moulded
with shoal of goldfish, 17cm.
high.   £453

VASES
LALIQUE

'Poivre', a Lalique smoked glass vase modelled with fruiting vine, 10in. high.
£580

'Bacchantes', a Lalique opalescent glass vase moulded in relief with naked female dancing figures, 24.5cm. high.
£8,250

A Lalique amber oviform vase, Gros Scarabees, engraved signature R. Lalique, France, No. 892, 29.4cm. high.
£6,600

A Lalique conical flower vase with intaglio moulded rose design, signed, 9¼in. high.
£120

'Soucis', a Lalique blue opalescent glass vase in clear and satin finished glass, 17.2cm. high.
£540

'Martins Pecheurs', a black Lalique vase, with impressed signature R. Lalique, 23.5cm. high.
£5,280

A Lalique vase, the satin finished glass moulded with marguerites, highlighted with amber staining, 20.5cm. high.
£550

An opalescent blue stained glass vase by Lalique entitled Salmonides.
£2,000

'Danaides', a Lalique vase moulded with six nude maidens pouring water from urns, 18.3cm. high.
£1,540

VASES
LALIQUE

'Gui', a Lalique opalescent glass vase, the body moulded with mistletoe, traces of blue staining, 7 in. high.   £462

A Lalique vase with four frosted figures of birds resting on groups of blackberries, 28.5cm.
£570

A Lalique opalescent glass vase, 'Lievres', 15.8cm. high.   £275

A Lalique clear glass stained vase moulded with grass-hoppers on blades of grass with blue and lime-green staining, 27.4cm. high.
£2,860

'Coqs et Plumes', a Lalique flaring cylindrical vase, 15.5cm. high.   £528

'Oran', a large Lalique opalescent glass vase moulded in relief with flower-heads and foliage, 26cm. high.   £4,400

An opalescent and floral engraved and blue stained 'Reflets' vase, by R. Lalique, France, circa 1928, 5in. high.   £200

'Aras', a Lalique opalescent globular vase, engraved France No. 919, 22.7cm. high.   £756

'Danaides', a Lalique blue opalescent cylindrical vase, the clear and satin finished glass moulded with naked maidens, 18cm. high. £864

VASES
LOETZ

A Loetz orange glass vase, designed by M. Powolny, 8in. high.   £150

Iridescent glass vase by Loetz, with everted tri-angular rim, circa 1900, 13.5cm. wide.   £950

Loetz iridescent glass vase with flared neck decorated with silver and pale blue banding, signed, 20cm. high.   £600

An applied and iridescent glass vase attributed to Loetz, 28.6cm. high.   £600

A Loetz pewter mounted two-handled iridescent glass vase, 8¾in. high.   £320

A golden purple iridescent glass pear-shaped vase attributed to Loetz, 30cm. high.   £270

A Loetz oviform vase, the body with four dimples, 25.4cm. high.   £825

A Loetz iridescent glass vase, the silvery-purple and green glass with tall tapering neck, 35.8cm. high.   £880

A Loetz white metal mounted baluster vase, the metallic orange glass with pulled loop metallic green and white decoration, 19.1cm. high.   £638

VASES
LOETZ

An iridescent glass vase attributed to Loetz, 9¾in. high. £260

A cobalt papillon iridescent shell-shaped vase attributed to Loetz, 18cm. wide. £380

An iridescent glass vase, attributed to Loetz, circa 1900, 18.75cm. high. £220

A Loetz vase, flattened bulbous base, with trailed and combed pattern in purple gold iridescence, 15cm. high. £1,404

A Loetz vase, the textured clear glass with gold iridescence on an amber ground, 20cm. high. £154

A small Loetz vase, with trailed decoration on combed iridescent purple wavy lines over a gold iridescent ground, 9.6cm. high. £972

A large Loetz vase with twisted body and quatrefoil neck, circa 1900, 43.6cm. high. £865

A Loetz vase, the body with four dimples and the rim and shoulders with deep blue pulled loop decoration, 13.8cm. high. £1,620

A brass mounted iridescent glass vase attributed to Loetz and the design in the manner of Hans Christiansen, circa 1900, 37cm. high. £540

VASES
MOUNT WASHINGTON

Burmese satin finish enamel decorated vase, Mt. Washington Glass Co., Mass., circa 1890, 4¾in. high.   £227

Late 19th century milk glass vase with floral enamelled decoration, possibly Mt. Washington Glass Co., 18in. high.   £100

Royal Flemish enamel decorated glass vase, Mt. Washington Glass Co., circa 1885, 6.7/8in. high.   £769

MULLER

A Muller Fres. Art Glass vase of baluster form in pink flashed with silver, signed.   £130

A vase in clear and frosted glass of ovoid shape, signed Muller Luneville, France, circa 1930, 20cm. high.   £180

A Muller Croismaire cameo glass vase, the shaded orange and amber ground overlaid with darker orange, circa 1900, 35.3cm. high.   £648

An unusual Muller Freres internally decorated glass vase, 24.5cm., 1920's.   £198

A Muller carved vase, the clear and satin finished glass deeply carved with a reclining tiger, 18.5cm. high.   £418

A Muller etched enamelled and gilt glass vase, circa 1900.   £264

232

VASES
OPALINE

One of a pair of opaline vases brightly painted with coloured flower bouquets, 49.5cm. high.   £1,400

A blue opaline tapering oviform vase with two gilt metal scrolling foliage handles, 20½in. high.   £300

A white ground opaline baluster vase with flaring neck, 12in. high.   £180

ORREFORS

An Orrefors cylindrical flared vase designed by Simon Gate, wheel engraved with naked maidens on classical columns, 17.5cm. high.   £528

An Orrefors vase, designed by Ingeborg Lunam, shaped like a giant bubble, 40cm. high.   £550

An Orrefors vase, wheel-engraved in neo-classical style, etched signature Orrefors 1930 S Gate 238 E.W., 17.5cm. high. £418

A large Orrefors engraved glass vase, 1940's. £300

An Orrefors large presentation glass vase by S. Gate and E. Wejdljch, 1928, 11¼in. high.   £1,400

An Orrefors engraved glass vase, designed by Vicke Lindstrand, 1940's, 23.5cm. £352

VASES
SEGUSO

A Seguso 'valva' vase designed by Flavio Poli, grey cased in amethyst coloured glass, circa 1958, 15cm. high.   £2,750

An Archimede Seguso vase, tomato-red cased with clear glass and with gold foil inclusions, circa 1960, 37cm. high.   £1,100

'Vaso a valva', an Italian glass vase, attributed to Seguso and the design to F. Poli, 23.5cm. high.   £540

STEUBEN

An Aurene vase by Steuben Glass Works, New York, circa 1920, 8in. high. £1,380

A Steuben green jade vase, Corning, New York, circa 1920, 10½in. high.   £325

A 20th century Steuben cased glass vase, Corning, N.Y., emerald green to white to gold Aurene interior, 10in. high.   £416

STOURBRIDGE

A Stourbridge cameo glass vase, the mid-blue ground overlaid in white and carved all-over with trailing wall-flowers, 12cm. high.   £700

A Stourbridge bottle-shape vase with wide trumpet mouth, of opaque white glass, 35.5cm. high.   £100

A Stourbridge olive-green opaline vase on four gilt feet detailed in white and black enamel, 12¾in. high.   £160

VASES
TIFFANY

A Tiffany iridescent glass
vase, 22.5cm.   £330

A Tiffany Favrile vase
of trumpet form, on flu-
ted domed foot with
folded rim, 33.5cm. high.
£1,980

Tiffany Favrile blue iri-
descent vase, New York,
circa 1920, 7½in. high.
£566

Early 20th century Tiffany
Art glass vase, New York,
4¼in. high.   £540

A Tiffany 'Favrile' vase, the
bowl of milky-white glass
shading to yellow decorated
with lime-green striated
feathers, 26cm. high.
£1,430

Early 20th century red
Tiffany glass vase with pulled blue iridescent design,
3¼in. high.   £1,620

A Tiffany Jack-in-the-Pulpit
vase, deep purple and gold
iridescent glass, 33cm. high.
£2,052

Tiffany blue iridescent Art
glass vase, New York, circa
1900, 3¾in. high.   £945

Tiffany Favrile gold iri-
descent vase, New York,
circa 1920, 6¼in. high.
£533

VASES
VENINI

A Venini 'vaso a Canne', flaring cylindrical shape with waved rim, circa 1950, 22cm. high. £1,980

A Venini 'Pezzato' vase designed by F. Bianconi, cigar shaped with patchwork decoration, circa 1960, 27.2cm. high. £4,320

A Venini 'vetro a file' vase, the russet coloured glass internally decorated with grey veining inlaid with purple rafia. £702

A Venini vase designed by Fulvio Bianconi, 1949, 21cm. high. £4,400

A Venini handkerchief vase in blue with a white interior, 9½in. high. £110

A Venini vase, clear glass cased over purple, 27cm. high. £702

A Venini 'Occhi' vase designed by Carlo Scarpa, the cased red, black and clear glass pressed together to form 'windows', circa 1955, 15.5cm. high. £3,456

A Venini cylindrical vase, composed of three equal cylinders of purple, amber and smoke-grey glass, 24cm. high. £825

A Venini vase designed by Fulvio Bianconi, concave lozenge shape internally decorated with a 'tartan' pattern, 27.5cm. high. £61,600

VASES
VENINI

A Venini vase designed by
Ludovico de Santillana,
the grey glass with irregular
applied white drips, circa
1962, 20.5cm. high. £220

A Venini 'vetro a Granulari'
vase, designed by Carlo
Scarpa, circa 1951, 20cm.
high.   £7,700

A handkerchief vase, attributed to Venini, cased glass
with alternating vertical
stripes in yellow and purple
latticinio, 14.7cm. high. £378

A Venini vase designed by
Carlo Scarpa, in plain tomato-
red cased with clear glass,
24.5cm. high.   £500

A Venini vase designed by
Thomas Stearns, asym-
metric bubble shape, circa
1962, 25cm. high. £4,620

A Venini vase designed by
Fulvio Bianconi, circa
1950, 32cm. high. £7,150

WEBB

A cameo vase overlaid in white
on a matt cranberry-red ground,
by Thomas Webb & Sons, circa
1885, 23cm. high.   £440

Late 19th century Webb
Burmese glass vase, England,
2½in. high.   £190

A Webb cameo vase of deep
funnel form, on everted
conical foot, circa 1910,
25cm. high.   £200

WAFER STANDS

A St. Louis patterned concentric millefiori wafer-stand, 3.3/8in. high. £408

À St. Louis macedoine wafer stand with ogee bowl, the base filled with parts of coloured canes and ribbons, 3½in. high. £540

A Baccarat close millefiori wafer dish, the base with a cane inscribed 'B1848', 10cm. high. £1,080

WALL LIGHTS

One of a pair of harlequin cut glass twin branch wall lights, 30in. high. £1,320

One of a set of four George III style five-light crystal wall lights, fitted for electricity, 23in. high, 21in. wide. £942

One of a pair of cut glass five-light wall lights, the nozzles with silver plated liners, 25in. high. £1,620

One of a pair of oak and leaded glass wall lanterns, circa 1910, 23in. long. £594

One of a pair of late 19th century mirrored red velvet wall sconces with clear diamond point lights, 16in. high. £200

A plique a jour and metal lantern, each panel depicting a female figure in the manner of Robt. A. Bell, 34.5cm. high. £1,728

WINE BOTTLES

An early sealed wine
bottle of olive-green tint,
inscribed Piffour 1726,
18.5cm.   £330

A wine bottle of dark brown
glass, of depressed spherical
form with kick-in base, circa
1710, 14cm. high.   £154

An early wine bottle of
dark-green metal, circa
1670, 19.5cm. high.
                      £440

A sealed and dated green glass
wine bottle of mallet shape
with conical neck, the seal
inscribed IOS Dalyzell and
dated 1738, 8¾in. high.
                      £400

Early 18th century sealed
wine bottle of olive-green tint
and onion shape, 18cm. high.
                      £440

A sealed wine bottle of upright
form and olive-green tint,
dated 1747, 21.5cm. high.
                      £286

An early sealed wine bottle in
dark green glass, bearing a
seal 'Thos. Abbott 1728',
19.5cm. high.   £720

A sealed wine bottle of upright
form and olive-green tint, the
body with a seal inscribed M
Stripp/Lyskerd, circa 1745,
23.5cm. high.   £154

An early sealed wine
bottle of 'globe-and-
shaft' form, perhaps
circa 1650, 19.5cm.
                    £3,000

WINE BOTTLES

A sealed wine bottle, inscribed 'Nicholas Pratt Exton, 1731', 20cm.
£231

An early English wine bottle with treacle glaze, 6½in., circa 1700.   £55

A tappit hen sealed cylindrical wine bottle, 1771, 31cm. high.   £324

An early 18th century green glass sealed wine bottle, 20cm. high.   £175

An early Dutch 'onion' bottle, 7in. high.   £35

17th century Dutch sealed wine bottle shoulder applied with armorial seal, 9½in. high.   £1,500

WINE GLASS RINSERS

An Irish wine glass rinser, circa 1790, 9.8cm. high.   £495

Two of ten George III wine glass rinsers, circa 1810, 5in. diam.   £386

One of a set of six wine glass coolers/rinsers.   £70

WINE GLASSES

A wine glass with round
funnel bowl, 7in. high.
£180

A Newcastle airtwist wine
glass with a funnel bowl,
on a domed foot, circa
1755, 16cm. high. £151

A composite stemmed
wine glass with round
funnel waisted bowl,
circa 1750, 16cm. high.
£97

A George III wine glass with
facet cut stem and tapering
bowl, circa 1775, 6.1/8in.
high.   £128

A wine glass by David Wolff,
the stem cut with diamond
facets, 1790-95, 15cm. high.
£3,780

A 'Newcastle' baluster wine
glass on a wide conical foot,
19.2cm. high.   £420

A deceptive wine glass, the
thickened ogee bowl set on
a double-series opaque-twist
stem, circa 1760, 14cm.
high.   £528

A dark green tinted wine
glass with ribbed cup-shaped
bowl, circa 1765, 12.5cm.
high.   £660

An armorial light baluster
wine glass, the funnel bowl
engraved with the arms of
Schieland, circa 1760,
18.2cm. high.   £972

WINE GLASSES

A tartan-twist wine glass with bell bowl, circa 1775, 16cm. high.
£594

A composite stemmed wine glass of drawn-trumpet shape, circa 1750, 16cm. high.
£140

An engraved airtwist wine glass with bell bowl, circa 1765, 16.5cm. high.
£162

An engraved opaque twist wine glass, the stem with opaque corkscrew core entwined by two spiral threads, circa 1770, 15cm. high.
£540

A baluster deceptive wine glass, the thick-walled flared funnel bowl set on a cushion knop above a plain stem, circa 1705, 11.5cm. high.
£388

A light baluster wine glass engraved by Jacob Sang, Amsterdam, 1757, 19.2cm. high.
£6,480

A colour-twist wine glass the bell bowl set on a double-series opaque-twist stem, circa 1770, 17cm. high.
£572

An 18th century commemorative wine glass with ogee bowl, 5in. high.
£250

A George III wine glass, the plain stem with single series opaque twist, with saucer-top bowl, circa 1760, 6½in. high.
£141

WINE GLASSES

A green tinted wine glass, the double ogee bowl on a plain stem, circa 1770, 15cm. high.   £280

A baluster wine glass with bell bowl, circa 1710, 15.6cm. high.   £154

A Dutch-engraved armorial baluster glass with funnel bowl, circa 1700, 21cm. high.   £1,296

Bohemian wine glass with funnel bowl, slightly chipped, circa 1730, 14cm. high. £450

Mid 18th century Bohemian armorial wine glass with flared faceted bowl, 14.5cm. high.   £400

A green-tinted wine glass with ovoid bowl set on a hollow stem, 1750-70, 15.6cm. high.   £242

An 18th century engraved wine glass on facet cut stem with central knop.   £260

A light baluster dated betrothal wine glass by the monogrammist ICL, 1753, 19.7cm. high.   £2,160

A composite stemmed wine glass of drawn trumpet shape, circa 1750, 18cm. high.   £129

GLASS

A mixed-twist wine glass with conical foot, circa 1760, 15.5cm. high. £352

An opaque twist wine glass, the ogee bowl with hammered flute to the lower part on double series stem, 6¼in. high.   £143

One of a pair of ogee shaped wine glasses, 5¼in. high. £121

Late 18th/early 19th century coloured wine glass of dark blue/green tint with bucket shaped bowl, 15cm. high.
                £165

A George III wine glass, the plain stem with double series opaque twist, part-fluted tapering bowl, circa 1760, 5.3/8in. high.   £154

A baluster wine glass, the funnel bowl with solid base on conical folded foot, 16.5cm. high.   £240

A colour twist wine glass with generous bell bowl, circa 1760, 17.5cm. high.
                £1,296

A composite-stemmed wine glass consisting of drawn-trumpet bowl with multi-spiral air-twist shank, circa 1750, 18cm. high.   £209

A colour twist wine glass with waisted bucket bowl, circa 1760, 17cm. high.
                £1,944

WINE GLASSES

An engraved tartan-twist wine glass with funnel bowl, circa 1770, 14cm. high. £475

A wine glass with funnel bowl and folded conical foot, circa 1730, 17.8cm. high. £286

A wine glass with rounded funnel bowl, hammer moulded round lower half, circa 1755, 16.8cm. £132

A colour twist wine glass with bell bowl, circa 1760, 16.5cm. high. £756

A wine glass with ovoid bowl, by David Wolff, The Hague, 1780-90, 15.3cm. high. £2,592

A Dutch light baluster wine glass, the ogee bowl engraved with a man-o'-war, 7in. high, circa 1750. £330

A baluster wine or cordial glass with waisted bowl, circa 1710, 16.3cm. high. £352

An incised twist wine glass, the bell bowl with honey-comb-moulded lower part, circa 1760, 17.5cm. high. £259

A mixed-twist wine glass, the bowl with rounded base and everted rim, circa 1760, 16cm. high. £143

WINE GLASSES

An emerald-green wine glass with ovoid bowl, on a plain stem, circa 1760, 14cm. high.
£108

A baluster wine glass with bell bowl, circa 1720, 16.3cm. high.
£209

An engraved wine glass with ogee bowl, circa 1780, 16cm. £638

A baluster wine glass, the bell bowl with a small tear to the solid lower part, circa 1715, 14cm. high.
£280

A colored wine glass of blue/green tint, the double ogee bowl supported on a plain stem and foot, circa 1765, 15cm. high. £770

A canary twist wine glass with pan-topped funnel bowl, circa 1760, 14.5cm. high. £2,592

A wine glass, the opaque twist stem with a pair of six-ply spiral bands outside lace twist, 13.5cm. high. £320

An incised twist wine glass with generous funnel bowl, on a conical foot, circa 1760, 14cm. high. £162

A mixed-twist wine glass with bell bowl, on conical foot, circa 1760, 17.5cm. high. £165

WINE GLASSES

English baluster wine
glass, 1720's, 16cm.
high.   £600

A cut cased wine glass, by
E. Bakalowits, Vienna, 8in.
high, circa 1908.   £1,000

An engraved airtwist wine
glass of drawn-trumpet
shape, on a plain foot,
circa 1750, 14cm. high.
                      £250

A plain stemmed landscape
wine glass by David Wolff,
on a plain stem and conical
foot, The Hague, 1790,
15cm. high.   £5,940

Mid 18th century pale-green
tinted wine glass for the
European market, 16cm.
high.   £176

A 'Lynn' opaque twist wine
glass on a conical foot, circa
1770, 14.5cm. high.   £462

Early 18th century
Bohemian engraved wine
glass with bell bowl,
15.5cm. high.   £800

A 'Lynn' wine glass with
rounded funnel bowl, circa
1760, 14cm. high.   £198

An engraved composite
stemmed wine glass of drawn
trumpet shape, circa 1750,
17.5cm. high.   £462

WINE GLASSES

A gilt wine glass, the facet-cut stem with central swelling, circa 1770, 16cm. high. £209

A facet stemmed friendship wine glass by Jacob Sang, 1761, 17.8cm. high. £8,100

Mid 18th century Silesian engraved wine glass with flared bowl, 14cm. high. £700

A 'Lynn' opaque twist wine glass with horizontally ribbed ogee bowl, circa 1775, 14cm. high. ·£345

A faceted stemmed portrait wine glass, by David Wolff, The Hague, 1780-85, 15.8cm. high. £5,184

An air-twist wine glass, 5¼in. high. £100

A small wine glass supported on a plain stem, 5¾in. high, circa 1770. £82

A 'Lynn' opaque twist glass with horizontally ribbed ogee bowl, circa 1770, 14cm. high. £496

A wine glass with large ogee bowl, 6¼in. high, circa 1760. £66

WINE GLASSES

A baluster wine glass, the bell bowl with a tear to the lower part, circa 1720, 15.5cm. high. £330

An opaque twist wine glass with ogee bowl, 5¼in. high. £100

A small wine glass, the ogee bowl engraved with a wild flower and bird, 5½in. high, circa 1770. £82

An opaque twist deceptive cordial glass with thick-walled ogee bowl, circa 1770, 14cm. high. £453

A plain stemmed wine glass with ovoid bowl decorated with a nude putto, by D. Wolff, The Hague, circa 1790, 14cm. high. £3,240

A colour twist wine glass with bell bowl, circa 1760, 17cm. high. £734

An armorial wine glass of drawn trumpet shape, circa 1740, 18cm. high. £1,540

A quadruple knopped opaque twist wine glass, the bell bowl supported on a double series opaque twist stem with four knops, circa 1770, 17cm. high. £308

A Williamite baluster wine glass with trumpet-shaped bowl, 18th century, 17.5cm. high. £1,404

WINE GLASSES
BEILBY

Beilby opaque twist
wine glass with ogee
bowl, 1765-70.
£3,500

Beilby opaque twist wine
glass, funnel bowl enamelled in white with goats,
1765-70, 15cm. high.
£2,750

Beilby opaque twist wine
glass, enamelled with a
hunting scene, 1765-70,
14.5cm. high.   £2,750

One of a pair of Beilby
opaque twist wine glasses,
enamelled with Classical
ruins, 1765-70, 15cm. high.
£2,500

A Beilby opaque twist wine
glass, the funnel bowl enamelled in white with floral swags
pendant from the rim, circa
1770, 15.5cm. high. £1,045

One of a pair of Beilby
opaque twist wine
glasses, 1765-70, 15.3cm.
high.   £3,000

Beilby opaque twist wine
glass, bowl enamelled in
white, 13.5cm. high,
1765-70.   £2,250

A Beilby opaque twist wine
glass, the funnel bowl decorated in white with a border
of fruiting vine, circa 1770,
15cm. high.   £907

Beilby opaque twist wine
glass with funnel bowl
enamelled in white,
1765-70, 15cm. high.
£2,500

WINE GLASSES
JACOBITE

A Jacobite light-baluster
wine glass with funnel
bowl, circa 1750, 18.5cm.
high.   £715

Airtwist Jacobite wine
glass, the funnel bowl
with a bird among fruit-.
ing vine, circa 1750,
15cm. high.   £108

A Jacobite wine glass of
drawn-trumpet form
with air-twist stem,
15.5cm.   £150

A disguised Jacobite glass,
inscribed 'The Immortal
Memory', circa 1750, 16cm.
high.   £1,540

An engraved colour twist
wine glass of Jacobite significance, the rounded bowl
with a rosebud, circa 1765,
13cm. high.   £453

A Jacobite wine glass, the
flared bucket bowl decorated with multi-petal rose and
bud, circa 1750, 16.5cm.
high.   £605

A plain stemmed Jacobite
wine glass, the funnel bowl
with a seven-petalled rose
and a bud, circa 1750, 15cm.
high.   £302

An engraved airtwist wine
glass of Jacobite significance,
circa 1750, 14.5cm. high.
                    £324

A Jacobite wine glass with
mercury-twist stem and
conical foot, circa 1750.
16cm. high.   £231

WINE GLASSES
JACOBITE

A disguised Jacobite wine glass with pan-topped bowl, circa 1750, 15.5cm. high. £352

A Jacobite wine glass supported on a double-knopped multi-spiral air-twist stem, circa 1750, 16cm. £352

A Jacobite wine glass with funnel bowl, circa 1750, 16cm. high. £286

A Jacobite airtwist wine glass, the stem with swelling waist knop filled with airtwist spirals, 16.5cm. high. £518

A Jacobite airtwist wine glass, the funnel bowl engraved with a rose and bud, circa 1750, 15cm. high. £540

A Jacobite portrait glass, the funnel bowl engraved with a portrait of Prince Charles Edward, circa 1750, 15.5cm. high. £1,210

An engraved light baluster wine glass of possible Jacobite significance, circa 1750, 18cm. £1,210

An opaque twist Jacobite wine glass, the bell bowl engraved with a rose, circa 1770, 17.5cm. high. £237

A facet stem wine glass of Jacobite significance, 5¾in. high. £94

Abbott, Thos. 239
Acet Distill 21
Adams & Barrett 126
Adams-Jefferson 83
Aigrettes 224
Albert 224
Ale Glasses 13
Alexandra, Queen 127
Alicante 224
Amberina 55, 66
Annagrun 89
Apothecary Boxes 14
Apsley Pellatt 172
Aras 229
Archer 43, 44
Argy-Rousseau 15, 25, 36, 73, 114, 109, 208
Argy-Rousseau Vases 208
Arsale 206
Arts & Crafts 54
Ashbee, C. R. 60
Ashtrays 15
'Aylesbury Patent 125

BP Super 152
Baccarat 46, 134-139, 168, 196-199, 238
Baccarat Weights 134-139
Bacchantes 227, 228
Bacchus 131, 132
Bahlia 76
Bakalowits, E. 247
Baur, Tobias 23
Barbini 68
Barnard, E. J. & W. 51
Barnard, W. J. 102
Barovier Vases 209
Barrett & Elers 125
Bartonsham Farm 123
Beakers 16-20
Behrens, Peter 105
Beijing 22, 180, 209
Beijing Vases 209
Beilby 13, 25, 60, 81, 196, 250
Beilby Wine Glasses 250
Beliers 224
Bell, Robt. A. 238
Benda, Eduard 19
Bentivoglio 83
Bercy 197
Berge, H. 68, 90, 133, 206
Bergh, Elis 202
Bianconi, Fulvio 206, 236, 237
Biemann 18
Billows Patent 124
Blackwood & Co. 100
Blazuiere, P. 70
Blondeau 170
Boers, B. 177
Boers, Bastiaan 89
Bohemian 18, 19, 20, 24, 30, 40, 46, 55, 62, 64, 65, 73, 82, 95, 96, 100, 106, 108, 122, 172, 188, 192, 193, 196-199, 209, 243, 247
Bohemian Vases 209
Bolin 53
Bonds 104
Borzoi Dogs 42
Boston & Sandwich Glass Co. 29, 57
Bottles 21-24
Bouchon 22
Bowls 25-35
Bowls, American 29
Bowls, Bohemian 30
Bowls, Daum 30
Bowls, Galle 31
Bowls, Irish 32

Bowls, Lalique 33, 34
Bowls, Loetz 34
Bowls, Pekin 35
Bowls, Venetian 35
Boxes 36, 37
Bradley & Hubbard 110, 115
Brandt, Edgar 111
Breadalbane 71
Breves Galleries 42
Bridge, John 26
Bristol 21, 57, 62
Burgess, J. 189
Burmese 26, 29, 46, 57, 111

Calcavella 63
Calcedonia 16
Caleys Patent 126
Camargue 225
Cameo Glass Vases 210
Candelabra 37
Candlesticks 38-41
Capstan Ink 101
Car Mascots 42-45
Carafe 46
Cartier 167
Cartwright & Woodward 64
Caskets 46
Castrol Oil 15
Caudebec 226
Cenedese 202
Centrepieces 46
Chamois 227
Champagne Glasses 50
Chandeliers 47-49
Chandler, C. 103
Chapman's Patent 124
Charder 37, 66
Chargers 66
Charpentier 196, 198
Cherry Chic 189
Chihuly, Dale 26
Christian, D. 153
Christiansen, Hans 50, 231
Cinq Chevaux 42
Claret Jugs 51-54
Cleveland 152
Clichy 107, 140-145, 167
Clichy Weights 140-145
Clutha 67
Codd 125
Codd, Hiram 21
Codd's Patent 126
Coley, S. J. 191
Colred 41
Compisizione Piume 46
Compotes 55
Comyns, William 103, 167
Congreaves 162
Connor's Patent 124
Copier, Andries 72
Coq Nain 42
Coqs et Plumes 224, 229
Coquelicot 75
Coralene 169
Cordial Balm 162
Cordial Glasses 56
Cork Glass Co. 67
Cream Pitchers 57
Cricklite 114
Cropper, J. 162
Crouching Mermaid 80
Crows Foot 64
Cruet Bottles 57
Cruets 58, 59

D'Argental 210
Daffy's Elixir 163

Dahlia 36
Dalby's Carminative 162
Dalyzell 239
Danaides 228, 229
Dans La Nuit 174
Daum 30, 105, 107, 108, 114, 116, 127, 130, 172, 178, 179, 211-214
Daum Lamps 116
Daum Vases 211-214
Davyz, I. 25
Decanter Boxes 59
Decorchemont 27, 28
Decorchemont, Francois 25
Decanters 60-65
Degue 113
Delatte 215
Delatte, Andre 111
Delfland 90
Delmester, J. 58
Deux Chevres 128
Diller, Thos. 70
Dimple Haig 24
Dishes 66-69
Dixon, James 58
Dockhead 82
Dominick & Haff 38
Dorset Mineral Water 191
Dr Hastings 164
Dr Lobb 163
Dr McMunn's 162
Dr Solomon's 162
Dr Wartburg's 163
Dragonfly 120
Dresser, C. 52-54, 58, 59, 166
Dressing Table Sets 70
Drinking Glasses 71
Drinking Sets 72-76
Drug Jar 105
Dubarry 170
Dufrene 110
Durand, Victor 27

Edgars Group Lotion 164
Edward, Prince Charles 89
Edwards, Charles 52
Edwards Patent 124, 125, 126
Egermann, F. 96
Elkington & Co. 54, 60, 61, 193
Elkington, F. 52
Elton 107, 108, 215
Epergnes 77
Epicea 226
Esso 152
Etling 80
Ewers 77
Exide 128
Eye Baths 78, 79

Faberge 25, 74, 170
Facon de Venise 17, 28, 68, 69, 82, 86, 96, 97, 177, 193, 195, 215
Falcon 43
Farrier's Guild 192
Favrile 28, 41, 50, 55, 74, 119, 179, 235
Federzeichnung 201
Ferro, Luciano 201
Figures 80
Firing Glasses 81
Fishers, Seaweed Extract 23
Flasks 82, 83
Fletcher G. H. 104
Floriform 68
Flygors 28
Ford Glass Co. 62
Formose 225, 226, 227
Fountainebleu 227
Franchini 170, 171

INDEX

Fratelli Toso 200
Fritsche 66

Galle 22, 24, 31, 36, 37, 66, 69, 77, 105-107, 116, 117, 165, 173, 176, 178, 179, 216-223
Galle Lamps 116, 117
Galle Vases 216-223
Garrard, Robert 58
Gazateur 190
Giles, James 173, 198
Gillinder 130
Glashutte, H. P. 68
Goblets 84-99
Goblets, Bohemian 96
Goblets, Facon de Venise 97
Goblets, Powell 97
Goblets, Sang 99
Goblets, Vedar 99
Goblets, Venetian 99
Goldrubinglas 30
Goodrich 15
Goodyear 15
Gorge de Pigeon 168
Goupy, Marcel 72
Grand Libellule 43
Greenock Apothecaries 189
Greenwood, Frans 91
Grenouille 43, 44
Gros Scarabees 228
Gruber, Jacques 186, 187
Gui 225, 226, 229
Guild of Handicrafts 36, 60
Gurschner, Gustav 113

Hald, Edvard 25, 167, 169
Haida, Fachschule 203
Hall, Samuel 121
Hampshire 115
Handel Lamps 118
Handyside, George 163, 164
Hannaford, E. 25
Harden 128
Harrogate Wells 22
Hawkes 39, 169
Heath & Middleton 51, 54, 73, 166
Heemskerk, Willem Van 23
Hennell, Robert 58
Henry's Calcined Magnesia 162
Hires 189
Hirons, Plante & Co. 51
Hobbs, Brockunier & Co. 153
Hobson, Diana 27
Hoffmann, Josef 27, 86, 207
Holdens 'Tommy' 163
Honeypots 100
Hop Bitters 23
Huber, Patriz 72
Hukin & Heath 51, 52, 53, 58, 59, 64
Humpens 100
Hutton, John 184
Hutton, Wm. 51, 62, 106

Ikora 115
Imperial Glass Co. 205
Ink Bottles 100
Inkwells 101-104
Iorio 114
Irish Bowls 32

Jack in the Pulpit 235
Jackson, Wm. 51
Jacobite 27, 56, 81, 84, 86, 87, 89, 176, 251, 252
Jacobite Wine Glasses 251, 252
Jacobs, Isaac 68
Jardiniere Acanthus 33

Jardiniere Saint Hubert 34
Jars 105
Jarvis, Thos. 187
Jelly Glass 127
Jones, E. S. 51
Jugs 106-108

Kane, Michael 128
Kaziun 130, 132, 133, 173
Kensington Glass Works 83
Knollys, Francis 87
Knox, A. 67, 192
Kosta 153, 202
Kothgasser, Anton 20

Lalique 15, 22, 33, 34, 36, 37, 40, 42-45, 49, 50, 64, 66, 67, 69, 73, 74, 76, 80, 102, 112, 128, 129, 131, 132, 174, 175, 178, 179, 224-229
Lalique Vases 224-229
Lamps 109-120
Landberg, Nils 63
Lanquedoc 225
Lanterns 121
Lauenstein 89
Lazzarino, Ferro 207
Le Verre Francais 110, 127, 178, 200, 201, 203
Le Verrier 113
Leerdam 72
Legras 203
Leleu, G. 110
Levrier 44
Lewes, J. 125
Leyuan, Zhou 182
Libbey 201
Liberty 60, 67
Lievres 229
Lily of the Valley 170
Limbo for Three 26
Limousin 111
Lindstrand, Vicke 72, 202, 233
Lithyalin 204
Lobmeyr 16, 17
Loetz 34, 113, 115, 179, 230, 231
Loetz Vases 230
Longchamps 43
Lorraine 211-214
Louttit 14
Loze's 191
Ludovico 237
Lundin, Ingeborg 25
Lustres 122
Lutz, Nicholas 131
Lynaris 24
Lynn 26, 62, 198, 247, 248
Lys 33

Ma Shaoxuan 182, 183
Madonna 21
Man in the Moon 31
Maps 190
Marinot 23, 129, 167
Marise 224
Martens, Dino 207
Martins Patent 160
Martins Pecheurs 228
Martiques 50
Marvin 113
Mason, T. 189
Masonic 81, 82
Matthews Patent 123
Maw's Eye Douche 79
Maxonade, Paris 178
Milano 57
Milchglas 17, 28, 65
Mildner, Johann 196

Milk Bottles 123
Millville 128, 132
Mineral Water Bottles 124-126
Miscellaneous Glass 127-129
Miss Pikes 163
Mitchells Patent 125
Mohn, G. Samuel 196
Molinard 174
Mordan, S. 166
Mordant, F. 102
Morning Glory 133
Moser 86, 204
Mother 45
Mount Washington 57, 77, 110, 131, 232
Mountain Dew 199
Mugs 192, 193
Muller Freres 112, 113, 232
Muller Vases 232

MacDougall, J. W. 123
Mackintosh, Charles, Rennie 187
McMunns, Dr 162
McPherson, W. J. 185

Nailsea 46, 83, 106, 108, 129
Nancy 30, 80, 129, 211-214
Nasson, Aldo 205
National Benzole 152
Neffe, Meyr 204
Neptune 204
New Bedford 113
New Bedford Glass Co. 197, 198
New England 130, 131, 133, 199
New England Glass Co. 57, 197
Newell, Steven 28
Nicholls & Plincke 106
Non-Such 68
Northern Dairies 123
Northwood Glass Co. 57
Nuremburg 176
Nuutajarvi Notsjo 201

O'Reilly's Patent 161
Ochsenkopf 16
Ock, L. 112
Odiot, Charles, Nicholas 54
Ondine Ouverte 34
Ondines 67
Opaline Vases 233
Optrex 78
Oran 229
Orange Julip 189
Orrefors 25, 72, 233
Orrefors Vases 233
Osiris 112

Pairpoint 112, 113, 118
Palissy 227
Palmer & Co. 110
Pansy 119
Paperweights 130-153
Parker Bros 190
Pearce, D. & L. 175, 183
Peche, Dagobert 87
Pekin 35, 205
Pelzel, Peter 202
Perche 45
Perruches 225
Pettifers Ewe Draught 24
Petrol Pump Globes 152
Pfeiffer, Anton 18
Pfohl, Karl 95
Phallenes 66
Pharaoh 44
Phillips & Pierce 52
Pierrot 80

Piffour 239
Pirelli 15
Pitchers 153
Plates 153
Poison Bottles 154-161
Poissons 227
Poivre 228
Portland 55
Poschinger, Ferdinand 205
Potsdam 17, 84, 85, 90, 91
Powell 60
Powell, Baden 202
Powell, James 65, 97, 103, 201, 206
Powolny, M. 230
Pratt, Nicholas 240
Pratts 152
Preissler 26
Prices Patent 22
Prince Charles Edward 252
Prutscher, Otto 71
Prytherch, David 26
Pullman Express 80

Quack Medicine and Cure All Bottles
  162-164
Queen of Scots 186
Quezal 120, 201, 203
Quine's Patent 160

Radam, William 164
Radam's Microbe Killer 23
Rampillon 226
Ranftbecher 20
Ravenscroft 108
Rawlings, C. 70
Red Ashay 42, 44
Redline Super 152
Reflets 229
Reichsadler 100
Reid, Colin 128
Reily, C. 51 54
Reynolds, Sir J. 187
Richard 202
Richardson 77, 91
Robart 94
Robart, Willem O. 92
Robertson, Sanderson & Co. 199
Roemers 165
Roger et Gallet 170
Rosace Figurines 174
Rosalinglas 20
Roses de France 218
Round, John 53
Royal Flemish 77
Roycroft 115
Rummers 165
Ruspinis Styptic 162
Rylands Patent 124

Sabino 203
Saint Christopher 42
Saint Vincent 33, 178
Sale Bros, M. 114
Salmonides 228
Salviati 80
Sampson Mordan 166
Sandwich 109, 131
Sandwich Clambroth 40
Sandwich Glass Co. 57
Sang, Jacob 98, 242, 248
Sang, Simon J. 87
Sanglier 44
Santillana 237
Sardine Box 37
Savory's Patent 161
Saxton, W. H. 207
Scarpa, Carlo 236, 237

Scent Atomisers 165
Scent Bottles 166-175
Schiaparelli 171
Schieland 241
Schmelzglas 25
Schneider 108, 128, 200
Schneider, Charles 66
Schott & Gen. Jenaer Glas 76, 195
Schwarzlot 17, 26, 73
Schweppes 190
Seguso, Archimede 46
Seguso Vases 234
Seltzogene 190
Serving Bottles 176, 177
Shades 178, 179
Shell 152
Shi Chuan 182
Silesian 16, 17, 57, 89, 94, 248
Simmons, Wm. 58
Sinclaire, H. P. 38
Sirene 67
Six Figures et Masques 224, 227
Smith Bros 106
Smith, John 15
Snuff Bottles 180-183
Soucis 228
Spaco Ltd 189
Sparklets 189, 191
Spirit of the Wind 42, 43, 45
St Anthony 130
St Christopher 132
St Joseph 138
St Louis 129, 146-151, 238
St Louis Weights 146-151, 166
St Petersburg 130, 169
St Stephen 184
Stained Glass 184-187
Stangenglas 188
Stearns, Thomas 237
Steuben 26, 27, 39, 112, 234
Steuben Vases 234
Storer, G. 54
Stourbridge 52, 234
Stourbridge Vases 234
Story of Joseph 185
Stripp, M. 239
Submarine Poison 160
Summers, Wm. 70
Sunderland 165
Sutcliffe & Fewings 126
Sutcliffe's Patent 124
Suzanne 80
Sweetmeat Glasses 188
Swingewood 71
Syphons 189-191
Syrup Dispensers 189

Tankards 192, 193
Tantalus 194
Tapio Wirkkala 67
Taylors Mustard 21
Tazzas 195
Teapots 195
Tete de Coq 42, 45
Tete de Belier 43
Thatcher Milk Protector 123
Thomas, G. 22
Thorpe, Dorothy 127
Three Dahlias 36
Three Graces 184
Tiefschnitt 19, 95, 193
Tieze, Franz 52
Tiffany 28, 41, 46, 50, 55, 68, 74,
  104, 119, 127, 175, 179, 235
Tiffany Lamps 119, 120
Tiffany Vases 235
Toledo 153

Tonnelet 83
Toso, Aureliano 201
True Cephalic Snuff 162
Tudric 60
Tumblers 196-199
Turlington, Robt. 163
Tyrolean Dancers 170

Undene 129
Union Glass Co. 62

Val Saint Lambert 206
Vallerysthal 204
Van Dyke 28
Vases 200-237
Vedar 99
Veilleuse 109
Venetian 35, 99, 106, 168, 200
Venini 25, 27, 46, 61, 62, 63, 107,
  108, 236, 237
Venini Vases 236, 237
Ver Centre 206
Verlys 200
Vetro Pesante Inciso 46, 61, 62
Victoire 44
Victoria Wine Company 191
Vincent 111
Violette de Parme 166
Violettes 224
Vistosi 202, 205
Vitesse 45
Voltaire 131
Vredestein 15

Wafer Stands 238
Wall Lights 238
Walter, A. 66, 67
Walter, Almeric 68, 90, 110, 130,
  133, 202, 206
Warners 22
Wasp Waist 161
Waterford 82
Waterloo 64
Waugh's Patent 126
Webb 52, 60, 63, 110, 113, 175,
  183, 237
Webb Vases 237
Weeks, L. G. 190
Whitefriars 104
Whitford, S. & G. 104
Wiener Werkstatte 71, 87, 207
Williams, Christopher 27
Wine Bottles 239, 240
Wine Glass Rinsers 240
Wine Glasses 241-252
Wolff, David 85, 241, 245, 247, 248,
  249
Woodall, George 201
Woodall, T. & G. 153
Worrall, Thos 46
Wragg, Job 189, 191
Wrights of Walkery 191
Wuon-Poong 15
Wyeth Collyrium 78

Yangzhou 181, 182
Yardley 171
Ysart, Paul 132
Yvelines 225

Zara 21
Zechlin 91
Zeiner, Lukas 184
Zhongsan, Chen 183
Zhongsan, Ye 183
Zwischengold 18, 95, 196, 197, 198
Zwischengoldglas 17, 18, 19
Zwischensilberglas 20, 196